R00179 62611

D1249247

HOW TO MAKE AND USE A TELESCOPE

The Amateur Astronomer's Library

Under the general editorship of Patrick Moore, F.R.A.S., F.R.S.A.—
a series of books designed for the intelligent amateur, fully illustrated
with linecuts and photographs.

A Handbook of Practical Amateur Astronomy, by Patrick Moore
The Planets, by Patrick Moore
A Guide to the Stars, by Patrick Moore
How to Make and Use a Telescope,
by Patrick Moore and H. P. Wilkins
Life in the Universe, by Patrick Moore and Francis Jackson
Radio Astronomy for Amateurs, by F. W. Hyde
A Survey of the Moon, by Patrick Moore
The Sun and the Amateur Astronomer, by W. M. Baxter
Astronomy and Space Research, by G. A. Chisnall and Gilbert Fielder
Naked-Eye Astronomy, by Patrick Moore
Life on Mars, by Patrick Moore and Francis Jackson
The New Look of the Universe, by Patrick Moore
The Amateur Astronomer's Glossary, by Patrick Moore
Craters of the Moon, by Patrick Moore and Peter Cattermole
Amateur Astronomy, by Patrick Moore

HOW TO MAKE AND USE A TELESCOPE

H. PERCY WILKINS, Ph.D., F.R.A.S.

and PATRICK MOORE, F.R.A.S.

W · W · NORTON & COMPANY · INC · *New York*

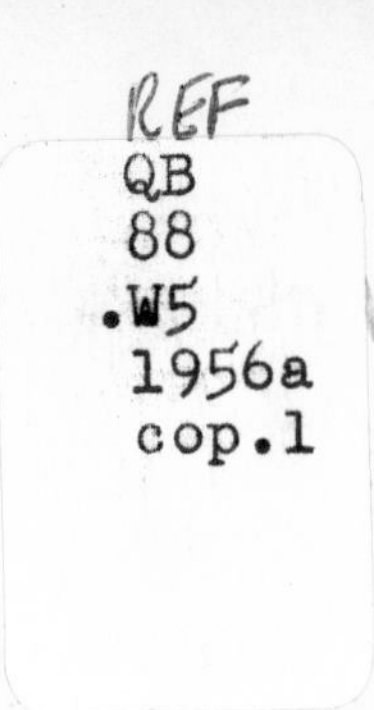

First published in England under the title
Making and Using a Telescope

Library of Congress Catalog Card No. 56-10091

ISBN 0 393 06323 2

PRINTED IN THE UNITED STATES OF AMERICA
FOR THE PUBLISHERS BY THE VAIL-BALLOU PRESS
0 1 2 3 4 5 6 7 8 9

CONTENTS

	Foreword	9
I	The Earliest Telescopes	13
II	Making a Telescope	22
III	Reflecting Telescopes	33
IV	Fitting up the Telescope	61
V	Some Refinements	76
VI	Eyepieces	86
VII	Using the Telescope: the Moon	95
VIII	Using the Telescope: the Planets	104
IX	Using the Telescope: the Stars	138
X	Special Equipment for Observing the Sun	151
XI	Photographs Through the Telescope	158
XII	Observatories	164
XIII	Using Large Telescopes	169
	Appendix:	
	A Suggestions for further reading	180
	B Useful information	185
	C Limiting magnitudes and test objects	188
	D Making a simple planetarium	190
	E Astronomical societies	195

ILLUSTRATIONS

1. Theory of the refractor 17
2. Newton's reflector 19
3. Simple altazimuth stand 27
4. Simple equatorial head 30
5. Hand drive for the equatorial 31
6. Grinding the mirror 41
7. Fining the surface of the mirror 44
8. Foucault test 46
9. Mirror cell—section with bracket 53
10. Mirror cell—back 54
11. Flat mount 55
12. Equatorial stand 64
13. Dials fixing 67
14. Sand clock or clepsydra 69
15. Thermal eyepiece 84
16. Oppositions of Mars 106
17. Phases of Venus 108
18. Antoniadi's map of Mercury 111
19. Terminator deformation on Venus 116
20. Typical false detail on Venus 117
21. Movement of the minor planet Astræa 124
22. Nomenclature of Jupiter 126
23. Saturn and its rings 131
24. Observing Mars with the 60-inch reflector at Mt. Wilson Observatory 171
25. Observing the planets with the Yerkes 40-inch telescope 175
26. Planetarium 193

FOREWORD

THERE have been many books written on the subject of telescope making; such works as *Amateur Telescope Making,* edited by A. G. Ingalls, are of course extremely well known, and are indispensable to the advanced student. So far, however, there seems to be no work which caters for the beginner who wishes to construct a small or moderate-sized telescope, and then use it to make useful astronomical observations. The present book is an attempt to fill this gap in the literature. If it encourages even one would-be astronomer to make an instrument of his own, and then contribute something to the great science, the authors will be more than content.

The book has naturally been planned, discussed and worked out by both writers, working in the closest collaboration. The second author wishes, however, to make it clear that the technical chapters dealing with telescope construction are almost entirely the work of Dr. Wilkins, and that Moore's contribution has been confined in the main to Chapters I, VIII, IX, and XII.

Our thanks are due to Miss Patricia Cullen, who has given great artistic assistance with many of the technical line diagrams, particularly those in Chapter III.

H. P. W.
P. M.

HOW TO MAKE AND USE A TELESCOPE

I

THE EARLIEST TELESCOPES

IT HAS often been said that astronomy is the oldest of the sciences. The statement is perfectly true; even the primitive man who roamed the dense forest of 25,000 years ago must have taken some notice of the wonders far above his head, while some of the early religions were based purely upon the worship of the celestial bodies. The ancient Chaldæans divided the stars into the groups of constellations that we still know to-day; the Chinese observed eclipses and comets, while some of the more enlightened Greeks realized that the Sun, not the Earth, was the centre of the planetary system.

Ancient astronomy was bound to be limited in scope, simply because the people of those times were forced to depend upon observations made with the eye alone. It was therefore impossible for them to make out many details. Even the Moon, by far the nearest of all the heavenly bodies, is about a quarter of a million miles away—a distance equal to ten times round the Earth's equator—while Venus, the closest of the planets, is a hundred times as distant, and the stars themselves are almost inconceivably remote. At such distances, close observation is clearly out of the question without optical aid.

Yet the ancients did succeed in finding out a great deal. By the end of the sixteenth century, when the first Queen Elizabeth ruled in England, it was known that our Earth—once supposed to be the most important body in the universe—is nothing more than a small, cool world or "planet" circling an unimportant star, the Sun; that the Moon is no goddess, but a secondary body or "satellite" keeping company with the Earth; that the bright "moving stars," Mercury, Venus, Mars, Jupiter, and Saturn, are other planets belonging to the solar family, and that the twinkling, cool-looking stars of the night sky are in reality blazing suns, many of them far more brilliant than our own. When we remember the difficulties under which they laboured, the achievements of our ancestors must be considered as most remarkable.

The principle of the ordinary refracting telescope is so simple that one is inclined to be surprised that it was not discovered until the seventeenth century, particularly as glass had been known from very early times, and spectacles had been in use since about 1270 (some authorities consider that they were invented by Roger Bacon, though the evidence is decidedly slender). It is also just within the bounds of possibility that the story of the telescope goes back to Egyptian times, and that the astronomer-priests of the Nile had developed some sort of optical instrument, the secret of which was later lost.

Bacon himself has been said to have known the principles of the telescope, and a similar claim has been advanced in favour of an Englishman named Leonard Digges, but the true history of telescopes begins in or about the year 1608, when Hans Lippersheim, a spectacle-maker of the little town of Middelburg on the Isle of Walcheren, announced that he had invented an instrument with which he could "see at a very great distance." On October 4, 1608, a committee sent from The Hague tested the instrument. Evidently they were satisfied, for on October 6 they agreed to give Lippersheim 900 florins for it. It has often been stated that the original discovery was accidental, but this seems dubious, and the question is in any case unimportant.

Before long, several telescopes seem to have been made and distributed in Holland and neighbouring countries. The first astronomical observations were, of course, those of the great Italian scientist Galileo Galilei, who first heard of the discovery of the telescope in May, 1609, while paying a visit to Venice, and hastened to copy and improve upon Lippersheim's work. At about the same time, telescopic observations were being made in Germany by Simon Marius, and in Great Britain by Thomas Harriot and Sir William Lower, but the work of these men is of secondary importance.

Galileo's own words, written in his *Sidereal Messenger* of 1610, are worth quoting: "I prepared a tube, at first of lead, in the ends of which I fitted two glass lenses, both plane on one side, but on the other side one spherically convex, and the other concave. Then bringing my eye to the concave lens, I saw objects nine times larger than when they are seen with the natural eye alone. I shortly afterwards constructed another telescope with more nicety, which magnified objects more than sixty times. At length, by sparing neither labour nor expense, I succeeded in constructing for myself an instrument so superior that objects seen through it appeared magnified nearly a thousand times, and more than thirty times nearer than if viewed by the natural powers of sight alone."

Galileo's greatest telescope seems a puny thing when compared with even a small home-made telescope of to-day. Yet in the years following 1609, Galileo made a series of discoveries that laid the foundations for all the work now in progress at the great observatories of Palomar, Mount Wilson, Meudon, and the rest. The wonderful panorama of the universe was spread before his astonished gaze. The craters of the Moon, the satellites or "Medicean stars" circling Jupiter, the spots of the Sun, the "infinite multitude" of stars in the Milky Way, the phases of Venus and Mars—all these were revealed to him; even the rings of Saturn were seen, though not clearly enough for Galileo to make out just what they were.

All pioneers, from Aristarchus in classical times down to the Wright brothers and Hermann Oberth in our own century, have had their detractors. Galileo was no exception. His discoveries seemed to prove that the new and revolutionary theory of a Sun-centred system was in fact correct; as such, they were frowned upon by the Christian Church. Some eminent men suggested that Galileo had bewitched his telescopes, while others refused to look through them at all. The story of how the great scientist was summoned to Rome and forced to "curse, abjure and detest" his theory of the universe is too well known to need repetition. However, the truth could not be suppressed indefinitely, and by the time that Galileo died, in 1642, the idea of an Earth-centred universe had been abandoned by all thinking men.

The theory of a simple refractor is shown in Fig. 1. The light from the object under observation is collected by a lens or "object-glass" (O.G.), and brought to focus at F, where it is magnified by an "eyepiece" (E). It should be stressed that all the actual magnification is done by the eyepiece, while the only function of the object-glass is to collect the light. The larger the object-glass, the more light can be collected, and therefore the higher the magnifying power that can be used.

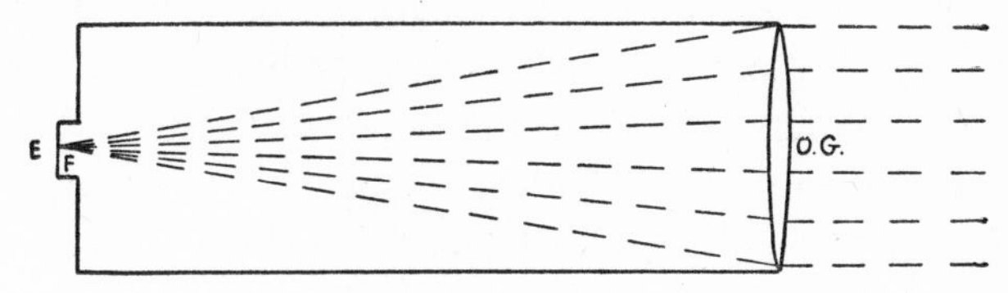

Fig. 1. Theory of the refractor

Modern telescopes are constructed so that any standard eyepiece will fit any telescope. It would therefore be possible to take an eyepiece of considerable magnifying power, suitable for work with a large telescope, and fit it into the tube of a small instrument—but it would be quite unusable, as the small object-glass would not collect enough light for the high power to be employed.

The convex-concave lens arrangement, used by Lippersheim and by Galileo, gives an erect image, so that the story of Lippersheim's seeing a distant weather-vane upside down is clearly untrue. It also produces an extremely small field of view. In his *Caloptrics,* of 1611, the great mathematician Kepler suggested an alternative arrangement, making use of two convex lenses. This system was found to give a far larger field of view, so that despite the lack of sharpness in definition, Keplerian refractors had come into general use by the middle of the seventeenth century. They were used by two of the greatest telescopic observers of the time, Christian Huygens of Holland (who discovered Saturn's sixth satellite, Titan, as well as the true nature of the ring system), and Johannes Hevelius of Danzig (who drew up the first valuable map of the Moon).

The distance between the object-glass of a refractor and the focal point is known as the "focal length." With the Keplerian refractors, the focal lengths were inconveniently great. Hevelius' most powerful telescope had a focal length of no less than 150 feet, and the object-glass had to be fastened to a mast 90 feet high! Huygens made a telescope of 210 feet focal length, and Adrien Auzout, who was instrumental in founding the French Académie des Sciences and in persuading Louis XIV to build and equip the Paris Observatory, is said to have constructed a telescope with a focal length of 600 feet. Needless to say, these instruments were cumbersome in the extreme, and it does not appear that Auzout's 600-foot arrangement was ever actually used.

One of the great troubles about the early refractors was the fact that they invariably produced a great deal of false colour around any brilliant object such as a star. This arose from the nature of light itself. "White" light is not nearly so simple as it appears. It is in fact made up of a blend of all the colours of the rainbow, from red at the long-wave end of the spectrum to violet at the short-wave end. All colours are not equally treated by the object-glass; red light, for example, is bent decidedly less than blue, so that it will be brought to focus at a different point. No solution to this difficulty was found for many years, and meanwhile the work of Gregory and Newton led to the construction of an entirely different type of telescope—the reflector.

In 1663 a Scottish mathematician, James Gregory, wrote a book entitled *Optica Promota,* in which he discussed the images of objects produced by curved mirrors. Gregory never actually built such an instrument (he had no practical skill, as he himself admitted), and the first true reflector was produced several years later by England's greatest man of science, Isaac Newton.

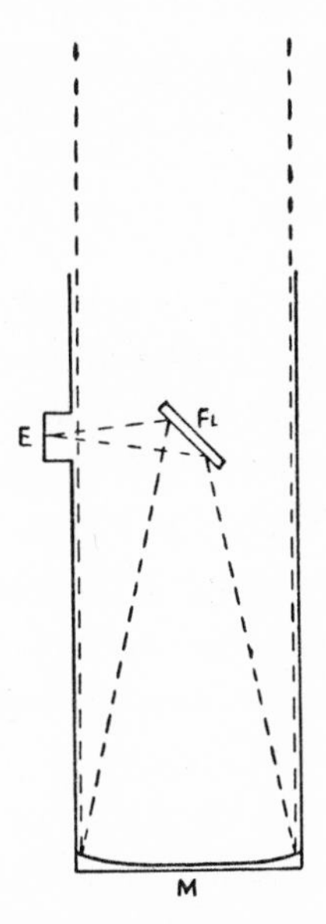

Fig. 2. Newton's reflector

Newton's arrangement is shown in Fig. 2. The object-glass of the refractor is dispensed with, and the light from the distant body passes down an open tube until it strikes a concave mirror or "speculum" (M). The light is reflected back up the tube until it strikes a smaller plane mirror or "flat" (FL), and is then directed towards the side of the tube, where it is brought to focus and magnified by the eyepiece (E) in the ordinary way. With a Newtonian reflector, therefore, the observer looks into the side of the tube. Gregory's suggested arrangement was somewhat different, and other types of reflectors were produced by Cassegrain (1672) and Herschel (about 1780), but these various modifications need not concern us for the moment.

With the reflector, the false-colour trouble that haunted the early workers does not arise—since a mirror makes no distinction between the light of different wave-lengths—and for a time, at least, the refractor seemed to be in eclipse. The first reflectors had mirrors of glass, but in 1732 James Short, of Edinburgh, commenced to manufacture excellent Gregorian reflectors with mirrors made of metal. Some of Short's instruments were of remarkably high quality.

Meanwhile, however, some interesting experiments upon refractors were being carried out by a wealthy Essex amateur, Chester Moor Hall. Hall argued that since the human eye corrects for the unequal refrangibility of light, it should be possible to construct a compound object-glass which would do the same—using adjacent lenses made up of different types of glass which would compensate for each other's errors. As a matter of fact, his theory was basically wrong, but it did lead him to the construction of an "achromatic" refractor with a compound object-glass 2½ inches in diameter and a focal length of only 20 inches. Hall seems to have had no wish for fame. He took no steps to make his discovery known, and it was only when the famous optician Dollond independently discovered the same principle, in 1758, that refractors could once more be considered upon equal terms with reflectors.

Subsequent progress was comparatively rapid. Between 1774 and his death in 1822, William Herschel, who started his career as a band-boy in the Hanoverian Army and ended it as Court Astronomer to King George of Britain, constructed reflectors which would bear comparison with most modern instruments—the greatest of them had a mirror 48 inches across; the ruins of the tube can still be seen at his old home in Slough, while the mirror itself hangs upon the wall in the hall of Observatory House, an eloquent testimony to its maker's genius. Meanwhile, the Swiss optician Guinand perfected methods of manufacturing optical glass, so that Fraunhofer and other telescope-makers were able to produce vastly improved refractors. The building of Lord Rosse's tremendous 72-inch reflector, in 1845, ushered in the modern age of great instruments—culminating in that triumph of modern science, the Palomar 200-inch reflector, finally completed as recently as 1948.

In only three and a half centuries, Galileo's tiny "optick tube" has developed into a glass monster capable of photographing the light of objects millions of light-years away —far beyond the confines of our own star-system. Perhaps for this reason, many people suppose that useful work can be done only by astronomers working with large instruments at great observatories. This is not correct. Anyone, no matter how little he knows at the outset, can turn himself into an astronomer; and anyone with a certain amount of patience and skill can construct a telescope for himself. Astronomy is the most fascinating of all studies; and it is well to remember that some of the world's greatest astronomers, including Sir William Herschel, started their careers as humble amateurs.

II

MAKING A TELESCOPE

THERE is no need for anybody to be without a telescope, for it is possible to make a simple instrument of the refracting type at trivial cost and with the minimum of labour. The telescope may not be perfect; it may show a fringe of beautiful colours around all bright objects to which the objects themselves can lay no real claim, and it may be usable with low powers only—but it will be decidedly better than nothing, so that even if a better instrument is subsequently obtained the simple and inexpensive telescope will still have had a use. Moreover, such a telescope is always handy for sweeping the sky, or for glancing at the Moon to see what formations are well placed and whether it is worth bringing out the larger instrument.

Let us first consider the most simple instrument it is possible to construct. The cost will be practically nothing. The object-glass is a single convex lens, being, in fact, a round spectacle lens of as long a focus as possible (somewhere between 4 and 6 feet) and with a diameter of about 1½ inches. With a lens of such small diameter and long focal length, the aberrations are of little account. We also want a long tube, which can be made up of two or more cardboard mailing tubes joined together so as to form a tube of length equal to the focal length of the lens. To find the focus, hold the lens in front of a piece of paper or cardboard and move it about until the sharpest possible image of the Sun is obtained, when the distance from the lens to the paper can be measured.

The cardboard tube should have an internal diameter slightly larger than the lens, so that the latter will slip in. Cut a piece of cardboard, bend it into a ring and slip it into the tube until it is about 2 inches from one end. Fix it into position, using a little glue or paste. The ring should be slightly smaller in diameter than the lens, which will then rest on it. If the lens is too slack in the tube itself, another ring of thin cardboard can be made and slipped into the tube so as to fit the lens all around. To prevent the lens from falling out, we want another ring, which should be made to an easy sliding fit; this is pushed down until it rests upon the glass. Before fitting up, the rings and the upper inside part of the tube should be blackened with India ink.

We now have our spectacle-lens object-glass fitted within the tube. Very possibly it may be necessary to join two tubes in order to form one tube of the required length, and this must be done with care. Cut a strip of cardboard, bend it into a ring with the ends just touching, and see that it will fit tightly into one of the two sections that are to make up the completed tube. The ring should be about 4 inches in width. Half of it is coated with glue, and pushed into one piece of tube; after this has set firmly, the other half of the ring can be similarly glued and pushed into the second section of tubing, taking care to bring the two sections into contact. A ringing of tape on the outside to cover the join will complete the operation.

At the eyepiece end of the tube, we must make up and fit a short piece of tubing constructed so as to slide easily to and fro within the main tube. This is for the purpose of focusing the telescope; the eyepiece itself is actually fitted to this short, sliding tube. The eyepiece can be picked up at any junk shop; alternatively, it can be made from any small convex lens of short focus. Once the eyepiece lens has been obtained, it is only necessary to make up a cardboard ring to hold the lens tightly within the sliding tube. The chief point to watch during these operations is to make sure that both lenses are square with the tubes: if one or both is set at an angle, it may be found impossible to see anything at all.

Having done all this, we now have a long tube fitted up with object-glass and eyepiece (for the sake of appearances, it is a good thing to apply a coat of grey or black paint or enamel). At the first opportunity, it can be tested—a simple stand to hold it steady is described below (page 28). Select some bright object such as the Moon, and move the telescope about until when you look up the tube you can see the bright object apparently resting on top of it. When you first look through the instrument, you will see nothing but a glare of light; but the correct focus can be found by sliding the eyepiece tube in and out. (Occasionally, it is found that the main tube has been made too long for the proper focus to be reached. The remedy for this is obvious!)

With an instrument such as this, it will be possible to see spots on the Sun,* the principal mountains and craters of

* It is, however, highly dangerous to point any telescope—no matter how low-powered—directly at the Sun. This fact cannot be too strongly stressed. See Chapter X.

the Moon, the satellites of Jupiter, and other objects which require little optical power for their detection. The Moon, particularly, will repay study. There will be a certain lack of sharpness and some false colour; but since the telescope will have cost less than a dollar and taken only a couple of hours to make, it must certainly be regarded as a good buy, and will give a great deal of pleasure and useful service.

Perhaps there will be an achromatic object-glass to hand, either found in a junk shop or else lying about in some long-forgotten corner. If this is the case, it can be used instead of the spectacle lens, and correspondingly better results will be obtained. A metal tube may be available to replace the cardboard one; at the worst, a tube can be made from sheets of brown paper, coated with ordinary paste and carefully rolled over a broom-handle or some other object of suitable diameter. Should the reader be situated so as to have neither paper nor broom, the tube could be a square one, made up of strips of wood. Anyone who really wants a telescope will certainly find materials of some sort out of which to make the tube.

An extreme case once came to our notice in which the would-be telescope maker did not have a spectacle lens, and found it very difficult to obtain one in his remote part of the country. He was not daunted, and actually made an object-glass by examining the bottoms of several tumblers and selecting one which was of reasonable uniformity of curvature, so that it produced a tolerable image. The tumbler end was fitted into a cardboard tube with a simple magnifying glass as an eyepiece, and with this crude and very simple device the lunar mountains and the moons of Jupiter were seen. Truly, this was a home-made telescope in every sense of the word.

Of course, it is not implied that the reader must begin in such an elementary style. Second-hand telescopes can sometimes be picked up cheaply; even if very imperfect, they will be found far superior to the simple instruments described above. It may be that the tube, the eyepiece rack, and perhaps the stand will be available, but the really important part—the object-glass—missing. In such a case, it is clearly worth while to purchase an object-glass and have it fitted.

In describing home-made telescopes, we have stressed the importance of selecting a simple lens of as long a focus as possible, because the images formed by the different coloured rays produced by the passage of white light through the lens will then be well separated, and will not seriously interfere with each other. However, a short-focus instrument has its uses, and the fuzziness can be reduced by covering up the edge portion of the lens with a cardboard ring. An instrument of this sort can easily be made from a magnifying glass of around 2 inches in diameter and 10 or 12 inches in focal length fitted into a metal tube —the tube being made from a piece of a cake-tin, bent into tube form and soldered. A simple lens of short focus will act as the eyepiece. With this affair, one of us was able to obtain good views of extended star-fields, the brighter nebulæ, and a small comet which happened to be on view at the time. The total cost was less than a shilling.

We now assume that the reader has a telescope, either home-made or purchased. The next step must be to make a stand or support. It will very soon be found that unless the telescope is rested upon something solid, it cannot be held steady enough for any object to be well seen. A stand of some kind is an absolute necessity. Many weird and wonderful devices have been suggested, but the vital point is to make the whole apparatus as rigid as possible.

Any telescope stand must be capable of allowing the telescope to be pointed to any position in the sky. It must also be able to hold the telescope in a rigid manner, while still easy enough in movement to allow a star to be followed across the heavens. It follows that the stand must permit up-and-down motion, so as to reach celestial objects of any altitude, and also motion in "azimuth," or parallel to the horizon. A stand which fulfils these two requirements, while requiring adjustment both in altitude and in azimuth for a star to be followed in its apparent movement across the sky, is known as an "altazimuth" stand, and can be made without any difficulty.

For our home-made telescope, a simple altazimuth stand can be made from three broom-handles fitted into three holes bored in a thick, round wooden disk. The disk should be from 6 to 8 inches in diameter, and at least 1½ inches in thickness. The broom-handles should be glued into the holes, and it is advisable to strengthen by screws; next, the disk should be drilled through the centre, and an upright piece provided with a screwed section of rod can then be arranged to rotate. The cradle to carry the telescope is pivoted on the upright. In this way the telescope can be placed on the cradle and secured by two straps, so that the instrument can be directed to any part of the sky.

The disadvantage of the simple altazimuth stand is that if a celestial object is to be kept in the field of view, the

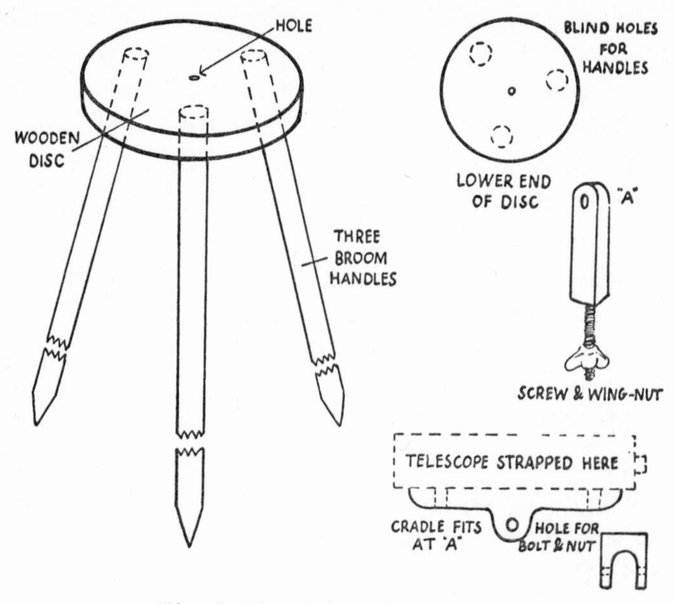

Fig. 3. Simple altazimuth stand

telescope must be moved in two separate ways—in altitude and in azimuth. An observer who erected his telescope at the North Pole would not have this trouble to contend with; from there, the stars revolve in circles parallel to the horizon, and therefore a simple motion in azimuth will keep them in view. Elsewhere, however, the stars appear to revolve round the northern celestial pole (marked approximately by the Pole Star) in circles which are inclined to the horizon, and continual adjustments in altitude are necessary. A moment's thought will show that if we tilt the tripod so that the upright ceases to be vertical, and points towards the Pole Star, we can return to simple motion in azimuth in order to keep a celestial body in view. All we have to do is to rotate the rod which was formerly upright, but which is now aimed at the celestial pole. Such a stand, known as an "equatorial," is a decided improvement upon the altazimuth.

Clearly, an ordinary altazimuth stand will become an equatorial when the azimuth axis is pointed towards the Pole Star, so that it is hardly more difficult to make such a stand than the simple form already described.

A simple equatorial stand can be made by modification of the upright, which is cut off so that one side is inclined at an angle equal to the latitude of the place of observation (41° 52′ in the case of Chicago).* The tripod is made as for the altazimuth, except that the upright is permanently fixed to the disk, while two small brackets are fitted to the inclined face. These brackets may be mere wooden blocks, but are better made of metal; they carry a rod, at the upper end of which is pivoted the telescope cradle. Once the instrument is set, the simple rotation of the rod in the bearings will keep a celestial body in the field of view. For a small and light instrument the upper bearing, that nearest to the telescope, could be a wooden block, with a semicircular hollow to take the shaft (which is prevented from coming out and is kept under light pressure by a metal or leather strap). The rod or shaft may also be of wood, carrying a pointed metal piece such as part of a large nail at its lower end; this pointed piece fits into a small hole, and the shaft can thus be rotated without difficulty.

All we want is something which will enable a rotatable

* Some other cities in the United States: Miami, Florida, 25°47′; New York City, 40°45′; San Diego, California, 32°43′; Spokane, Washington, 47°40′.

shaft to be directed to the Pole Star; the shaft itself must carry some sort of attachment which in its turn will allow the telescope cradle to move at right angles to the shaft, so that the range of view can be extended from the horizon to the "zenith" (overhead point) and even as far as the celestial pole itself. If the telescope is a heavy instrument, it will

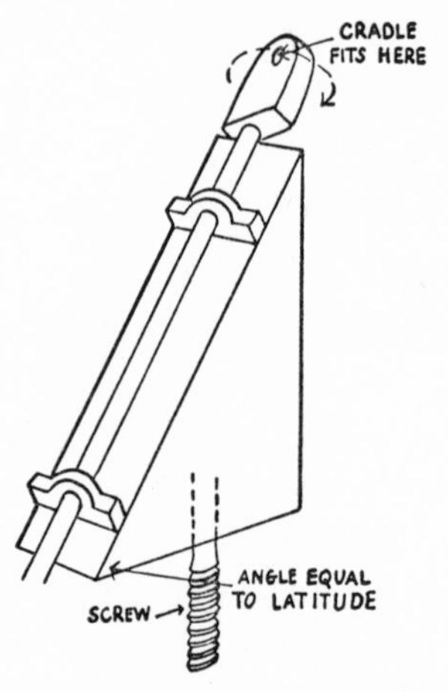

Fig. 4. Simple equatorial head

require balancing and instead of the cradle being pivoted to the top of the shaft it may be fixed to the end of a second shaft, which rotates in bearings at right angles to the polar axis. The balancing weight is then placed at the other end of this second shaft.

"Polar axis" is, of course, the name given to the inclined shaft—because it points to the celestial pole. The shaft at right angles to it is called the "declination axis," because it can be rotated so as to point the telescope to any declination, or distance north or south of the celestial equator.

Since the stars are in apparent continual motion across the sky, because of the Earth's axial rotation, we must keep on rotating the polar axis of our equatorial stand. This can be done either by hand or mechanically (by clockwork or electricity). If hand turning is used, a large wheel should

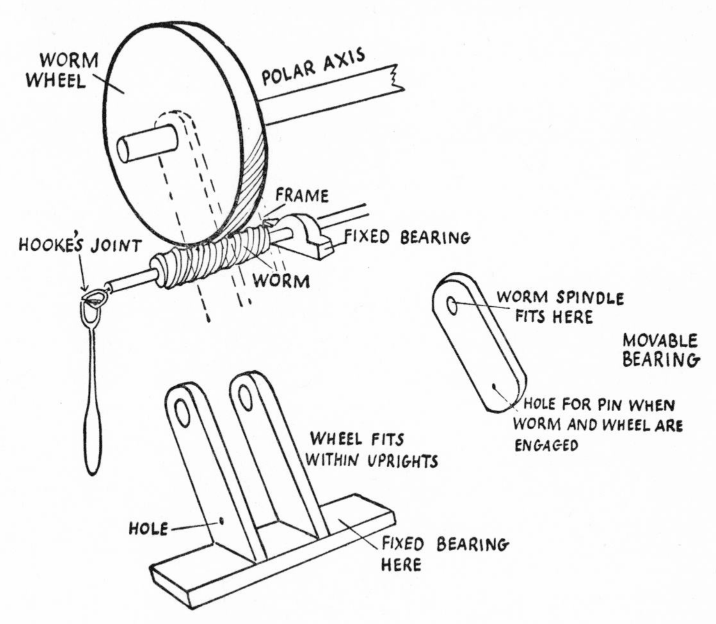

Fig. 5. Hand drive for the equatorial

be placed at the lower end of the shaft; this will be found easy to manipulate with cold fingers upon a frosty night! By use of a worm and wormwheel, a handle attachment can be constructed with a universal or "Hooke's" joint; but few people are likely to possess a worm and wheel.

Even if made entirely of wood, this simple equatorial stand will be found very useful later on when we wish to take photographs. For this reason alone, it is well worth the trouble of setting up—quite apart from its convenience.

Aiming the inclined shaft exactly at the Pole Star may present a little trouble; but once the correct position has been found, the positions of the three legs can be marked on the ground at the spot where the telescope is to be used. Three tiles or pegs will ensure that whenever the telescope is to be set up, the legs can at once be placed in the right positions, which means also that the polar axis must be pointing in the correct direction. Even the tiny spectacle-lens telescope will give much more satisfaction if mounted upon this type of stand than upon an ordinary altazimuth; and with such an outfit and plenty of enthusiasm for star-gazing, the beginner may look forward to many hours of pleasure.

III

REFLECTING TELESCOPES

ANYONE who wants a really powerful telescope at low cost must adopt the reflecting form of instrument. Not only are reflectors cheaper, but they are much easier to make than refractors of even moderate power; indeed, they can actually be made by any person who possesses considerable patience and a few simple tools.

In a reflector, the image is formed by reflection from a concave mirror instead of by a lens; the image is then examined with an eyepiece, which is really a low-power microscope, just as in the case of the more familiar refractor. In a reflector, the rays of light from the object under study first fall upon the mirror and are then reflected back as a converging cone to the focus; hence they pass along the tube twice. It is clear that since the image is formed so to speak "in the air" in front of the mirror, there must be some difficulty in arranging the eyepiece. It cannot be placed in the obvious spot; the observer's head would cut off most of the light rays coming from the star, quite apart from the disturbing effects of the heat of the human body. Various arrangements have been proposed to overcome this difficulty.

The simplest method is of course to tilt the mirror a little, so that the rays come to focus not in the centre but at the side of the tube, where the eyepiece is placed. This arrangement was proposed by no less a person than Sir William Herschel, discoverer of the planet Uranus and so-called "father of stellar astronomy." The observer has his back to the object under examination, and looks almost straight down on to the mirror. His head does not get in the way, but the tilting of the mirror introduces distortion in the image, so that the view is imperfect. It is true that the mirror can be designed for this off-axis form, but Herschelian reflectors are now uncommon, and are in any case too difficult for the beginner to attempt.

The Newtonian form has already been described in Chapter I. A small flat mirror is interposed a little way inside the focus, and inclined at an angle of 45°. The rays are thus bent at right angles, and the focus is found at the side of the tube, where the eyepiece is situated. With this type of instrument, the observer looks sideways into the tube. Though this attitude may seem unfamiliar, it is in fact most convenient, as the observer does not have to twist his body into peculiar contortions when looking at an object high up in the sky. On the whole, the Newtonian is much the best type of reflecting telescope, and is favoured by amateurs and professionals alike.

What are known as direct-view instruments, or compound reflectors, are arranged according to a different principle. The original scheme was due to Gregory. Instead of the flat mirror used by Newton, there is a small concave mirror, which is placed a little beyond the focus so that it reflects the rays back through a central hole in the large mirror. The eyepiece lies behind the main mirror, so that when using a Gregorian reflector the observer looks up the tube, as with a refractor. The image produced is erect. Gregorian telescopes can thus be used for terrestrial purposes; but unless effective shielding is introduced by day, illumination falls not only upon the main mirror but also passes through the hole, lighting up the eyepiece. A diaphragm pierced with a minute hole and placed in front of the eyepiece will cut off this troublesome sky-light by day, but it will also make the images produced very feeble and dim. Gregorian reflectors were very popular in the seventeenth and eighteenth centuries, before the discoveries of Moor Hall and Dollond paved the way for achromatic refractors; and all the telescopes built by the great optician James Short were on the Gregorian pattern.

In the Cassegrain modification, the small concave mirror of the Gregorian reflector is replaced by a convex mirror placed within the focus. These telescopes are extremely short, and give inverted images.

With both Gregorian and Cassegrain reflectors, the small mirrors must be ground and polished to a definite curve, which adds to the difficulty of making instruments of these types. Moreover, the adjustments are critical, while focusing is generally accomplished by moving the small mirror by a fine screw worked from the eye end of the instrument.

It is of interest to compare the four forms of the reflecting telescope. The front-view or Herschelian arrangement is basically the most simple, since it consists merely of a mirror and an eyepiece; but this advantage is offset by the distorted images, in which planets are misshapen and stars acquire "tails." Herschelian reflectors are hardly ever satisfactory.

The Newtonian type is usually adopted. The small flat

mirror does indeed cut off the light from the central part of the mirror, and some light is therefore lost; but there is no distortion of the image, while the definition is sharp and observing conditions comfortable. The Gregorian arrangement loses more light than the Newtonian; once again the small mirror is in front of the large one, and in addition the amount of light is further decreased by the eye-hole. Also, the small mirror is not easy to make, and the slightest departure from the correct curve introduces great distortions in the image produced. Cassegrain telescopes have disadvantages similar to those of Gregorians, though imperfections of the small mirror are not quite so disastrous.

Large reflectors can often be used either as Newtonians or Cassegrains; when this arrangement is adopted, a convex mirror is inserted in place of the flat. Sometimes, as in the case of the Palomar 200-inch telescope, the main mirror has a central hole. Alternatively, the rays from the convex mirror may be intercepted by a smaller flat before they return to the main mirror—thus being diverted to the side of the tube, where the image is viewed or the photographic plate is placed. This scheme was adopted for the 60-inch and 100-inch reflectors at Mount Wilson Observatory. It has the advantage that the equivalent focus of the telescope, and hence the scale of the images, can be varied within wide limits by using convex mirrors of different focal lengths.

Aperture for aperture, the refracting telescope is more powerful in transmitting light than the reflector. Moreover, with all except the giant instruments of great observatories the definition of the refractor is generally better; the light only passes once along the tube, instead of twice as with the Newtonian and three times as with the Gregorian or Cassegrain. There are no silvered surfaces to deteriorate, and adjustments are usually more or less permanent. Reflectors suffer more from atmospheric disturbances, and are also very sensitive to changes of temperature; from time to time they require adjusting, and the mirrors need periodical attention. On the other hand, reflectors are perfectly achromatic; they are easier to use, cheaper to buy, and easier to make. With care, they can be made to give every satisfaction, and are thus eminently suitable for the amateur observer.

Anybody who can use simple tools and who has a fair amount of common-sense can make himself a reflecting telescope. It is wise to adopt the Newtonian form; at least ninety-nine out of every hundred home-made telescopes are of this kind. Various points must of course be borne in mind. If it is to be kept in the centre of a city, or by the sea coast, the reflector will be under a disadvantage; the sulphur- or salt-polluted atmosphere will soon tarnish the mirror film unless it is properly protected when the telescope is not in use. It is unfortunate that such a film cannot be dispensed with, but glass is an inefficient reflector; the actual reflective surface is thus a thin film of silver or aluminum, the glass being merely to ensure that this film has the correct curve (that is, the parabola). In order to bring all the rays from a distant object to the same focus, the curved shape of the mirror must, of course, be very exact. Even then, the area of good definition is confined to a very limited region around the optical axis. The reflective film is easily renewed when occasion arises; under good conditions, it should last for at least five years.

If the reader merely wishes to have a telescope for very occasional use whenever anything spectacular comes along (such as an eclipse or a comet, or a close approach of Mars), and is not interested in the detection of fine detail, a small refractor of 3 to 3½ inches aperture is to be recommended. Should he be a more ambitious individual who wishes to see for himself such features as the delicate markings on Mars, the features of Saturn's disk, and the minute craterlets and clefts of the Moon, he must acquire an instrument of the reflecting type (unless, of course, he has several hundred dollars to spare). In what follows, it has been assumed that the reader wishes to make for himself a powerful telescope at as little cost of time, labour, and money as possible.

The first step in designing a reflecting telescope is to decide upon the size (that is to say the aperture or diameter of the main mirror), and the focal length. A useful size for a first attempt is a diameter of 6 inches, though an 8-inch mirror is of course decidedly better and requires very little extra labour in grinding and polishing. In the case of a 6-inch mirror, the focal length may be anything from 5 to 12 diameters (30 to 72 inches); with an 8-inch the same ratios apply, so that the focal length may be anything from 40 to 96 inches. However, it will be found that a short-focus mirror, with the focal length 5 to 6 times the diameter, is difficult to bring to a satisfactory figure. Any defects are far more injurious to the quality of the image, and in addition the deeper curve means that there is more glass to be removed by grinding and polishing, which means that the task is longer and more tedious. On the other hand, a long-focus mirror, with a focal length more than 10 times the diameter, means that the telescope is long and inconvenient, taking up unnecessary room, while once again the mirror is difficult to bring to a satisfactory figure owing to the fact that with a long focus there is very little difference between the spherical and parabolic forms. We should aim for something in between these extremes; a mirror with a focal length between 7 and 9 times its diameter is easiest to make. Our proposed telescope will have a focal length of 8 times the mirror diameter—that is to say 48 inches for a 6-inch mirror, and 64 inches for an 8-inch.

The first thing to do is to obtain two disks of glass, each with a diameter about ⅛ of an inch larger than that of the size of telescope decided upon. If we set out to make a 6-inch telescope, therefore, our two disks must be 6⅛ or perhaps 6¼ inches across; one disk is for the mirror, the other for the tool upon which the mirror will be ground. These disks may be purchased from any large glass merchant, in which case the edges will be ground; alternatively they may be cut from thick plate glass, when the edges will of course be rough, and will have to be smoothed by using a carborundum wheel and plenty of water. The disk for the mirror must not be less than one inch thick, or we may easily run into trouble later on in the process owing to bending or flexure. The disk for the tool may be considerably less—perhaps not more than ¾ of an inch thick.

In addition to the two glass disks, we shall want a few inexpensive items obtainable from a good hardware store. We must have carborundum powder (not paste): a 1-lb. tin of number 80, ½-lb. tins of numbers 120 and 180, and ¼-lb. tins of numbers 220, 400, and 600. It is not necessary to keep strictly to the above grades. All we want is a coarse grade to hollow out the glass and produce the rough curve as quickly as possible, and a sufficient number of finer and finer grades to remove the deep pits and scratches made by the coarser grades—thus bringing the surface into a condition such that the remaining irregularities will quickly polish out.

We also want 1 pound of good pitch, a rigid bench or stout stool around which it is possible to walk, a little beeswax and turpentine, and ¼ pound of optical rouge—either the ordinary red variety, which is messy, or a substance such as Cevri rouge, which is preferable inasmuch as it polishes more quickly than ordinary rouge and leaves no stains. The total cost of the two glass disks and the other materials need not exceed five dollars.

The principle of glass grinding to make an astronomical mirror is to secure one disk (the tool) to the bench, while the other disk (the mirror) has a wooden handle fastened to it; if the mirror disk is placed on top of the other, with carborundum powder and water between them, and is slid to and fro while the operator rotates it and also walks round the bench, the lower or tool disk will be worn away around the edge and will thus become convex, while the upper or mirror disk will be worn away in the middle and will thus become concave. We must give all the above-mentioned three motions to ensure that the disks shall be worn away evenly, and not on one side only, as would result from a mere sliding motion.

The handle of the mirror disk gives us something to

move the disk with. It may be made from a piece of an old broom-handle 3 to 4 inches long, with a piece of wood about 2 inches in diameter screwed on to it.

Having made the handle, gently heat the tool disk by holding it in front of a fire or at a safe distance over a gas

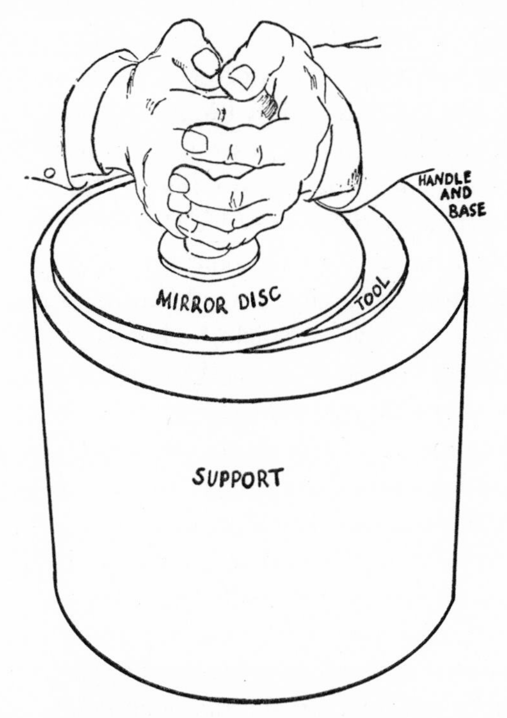

Fig. 6. Grinding the mirror

stove. Meanwhile, a little pitch should be melting in a small tin. Pour a little pitch on to the bench or stool, and press the tool disk firmly down. Heat the mirror disk, pour a little pitch on to the centre, and press the handle firmly down, taking care that it is right in the middle. With a carborundum stick and plenty of water, go carefully all around the edge, so as to remove the sharpness and produce a bevel; this will prevent a nasty chip in the unhappy event of the disk being accidentally knocked against anything.

Dip the face of the disk in water, scatter some No. 80 carborundum powder over the tool, and grind with the three motions. After about five minutes, lift the disk, add some more powder and a few drops of water, and continue grinding. The curve is rapidly produced, and after half an hour it is advisable to test to see how deep the curve has grown. During the grinding, the mirror disk is moved so that its centre approaches the edge of the tool.

We now have a curve of some sort, and of a certain radius. According to optical laws, the focus, or the distance from the mirror curve at which the image of a distant object is formed, is exactly one-half of the radius. Since we want our 6-inch mirror to have a focus of 48 inches, the radius of curvature will be double this, or 96 inches. The rough grinding should be stopped when the radius is 6 inches longer than this, or 102 inches.

To find out what the radius is, clean the mirror, set it on edge and swill with water. Now hold a light of some sort near the eye, and move it about in front of the mirror. If the reflection moves the same way as the light, the light is nearer to the mirror than the radius of curvature; if the light and the reflection move in opposite directions, we are outside the radius of curvature. In this way we can find the actual radius, at any moment, simply by experiment.

When the radius is found to be about 102 inches, the rough grinding is complete. Both tool and mirror must now be thoroughly swilled and scrubbed to remove every grain of 80 carborundum powder, and then the grinding process is recommenced, using grade 120 powder. Five or six doses of this, lasting about half an hour, and then the tool and mirror must again be cleansed preparatory to the change-over to grade 180 powder; subsequently, the finer grades of powder are used. The fine grinding should be thoroughly done; if it is not, and any pits from the coarser grades remain, they will take hours and hours to polish out. Altogether, the grinding will take about 4 hours, after which the radius of curvature should be slightly more than 96 inches.

Grinding completed, we must wash away every trace and every speck of carborundum powder, and clean and dry everything. Next melt some pitch in the tin, add a small piece of beeswax and make sure that the whole is completely melted. With string or tape, fasten a piece of waxed or greased paper around the tool so that it projects about 3/16 of an inch above the glass. Lightly wet the surface of the mirror and smear it with soap or rouge, so that it will not stick to the hot pitch. Pour the melted pitch on to the tool so as to form a layer of not more than 3/16 of an inch deep. As soon as the pitch has set sufficiently to retain its shape, rip off the paper band; then take the mirror, press it down firmly on the tool and move it about, if necessary pouring hot water over the pitch to soften it. After a time, the layer of pitch will have assumed the same curvature as the mirror. Never allow the Sun to shine on the pitch-tool, or it will certainly soften and flow over the edges.

Pitch is plastic, and slowly flows, especially when under pressure—which means that it is necessary to make some provision for its flow during polishing. This is done by dividing the pitch-covered tool into a series of squares of about 1¼ inch on a side; along the sides of the squares, the pitch is cut right through down to the glass, using a sharp

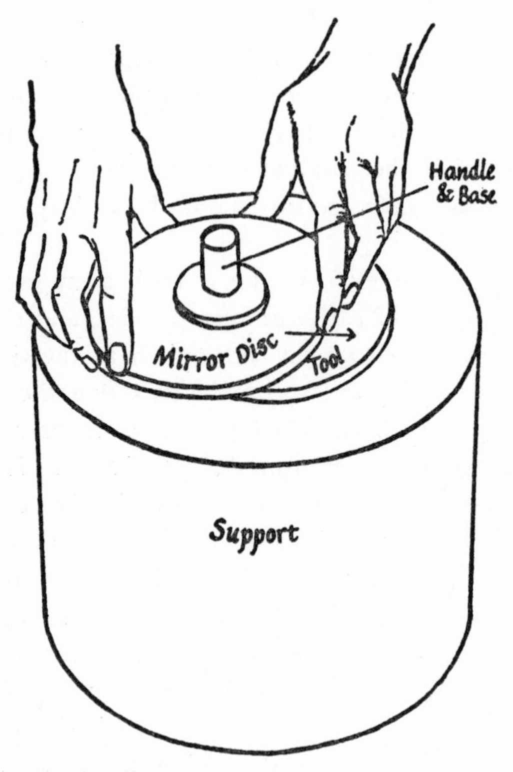

Fig. 7. Fining the surface of the mirror

knife, and the strips of pitch removed. The channels so formed act as air ducts, carrying away the spent rouge, glass particles and water, and allowing the pitch to flow. Sometimes the channels are completely filled up during polishing; when this happens, they have to be re-cut. It is very important to ensure that the centre of the tool comes neither in the centre of a square nor in a groove, but near one of the corners; otherwise, rings will almost certainly be formed on the mirror. It is also helpful to smear a little turpentine on the tool before applying the pitch.

The process of polishing is similar to that of grinding, except that rouge is used instead of carborundum powder, and the movement of the mirror over the tool is less. After a few minutes, a certain shine begins to appear, and in half an hour the whole surface should be semi-polished. Using a torch or a candle-flame, it is now possible to determine the exact radius of curvature with considerable accuracy. If the fine grinding has been properly done, no deep pits or scratches will remain, and the whole polishing may be completed in under 6 hours. The centre will be completely polished before the edge is even half finished; this is because the centre of the mirror is always in contact with the tool during working, whereas part of the edge is always in the air. Polishing should always be done indoors without any source of artificial heat nearby, as it is desirable to keep the temperature as constant as possible.

When the polishing is complete, we have a glass disk with one side flat and the other—forming the actual optical surface—concave. It must not, however, be thought that because the mirror is polished, it is ready to go into the telescope! The hardest part of the process is still before us. This is the figuring. Although we already have a mirror with a curve of some sort, which will thus form an image, there is only one curve which will give a perfect image free from hazy outlines and other defects: this is the "parabola," and if the curve of our mirror is not already parabolic it must be made so. There are several ways of producing a parabolic figure, but for the moment it will suffice to describe the easiest.

If the squares of pitch on the tool are in good contact with all parts of the mirror, and the latter is moved around but little (that is, with short strokes), the resultant curve will be what is known as a "sphere," or part of a globe. A parabola differs from a sphere inasmuch as it gradually deepens towards the centre; if therefore our curve is a sphere, we must deepen it in the middle. If the curve is not already spherical, it must be made so before modifying to the parabolic form.

The next thing we want to know is how to recognize the parabola when it has been produced. Fortunately, there is no difficulty about this, for once polishing is well advanced it is possible to determine what curve the mirror has at any given moment. For this purpose we require a simple piece of apparatus which can be made by anybody; it is known as the "Foucault" testing apparatus, after the distinguished French scientist of that name.

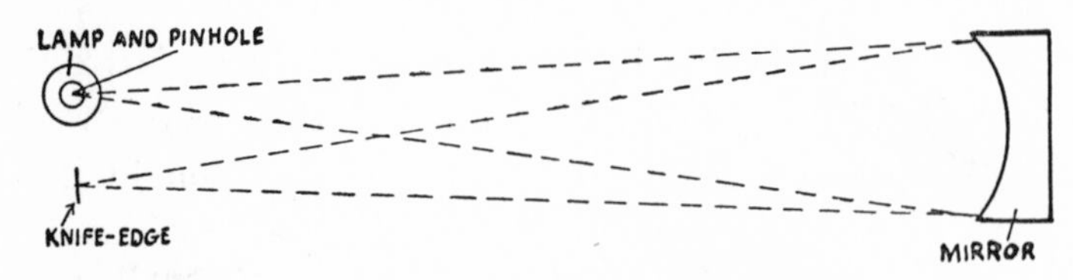

Fig. 8. Foucault test

The idea is to use an artificial star, in the form of an illuminated pinhole which is placed at the radius of curvature of the mirror. All we want is a small electric flashlight bulb surrounded by a metal tube which is pierced with a small hole, made with a needle point, and placed in line with the lamp. When the lamp is lit, the pinhole is illuminated, and becomes an artificial star. If the mirror is set up on edge in a darkened room, the light from the pinhole will fall on the mirror and be reflected back to the radius of curvature, where it forms an image of the pinhole. If the lamp is moved slightly to one side, the image will move in the opposite direction, and can then be caught upon a piece of card or a ground-glass screen. If we allow the image to fall on the eye, the mirror will seem full of light, like the full moon. Next, a knife-edge, such as an engineer's square or a safety razor blade on a stand, is slid across the image in front of the eye. What looks like a dark shadow will be seen crossing the mirror. If the lamp and eye are exactly at the radius of curvature, and if the mirror is a sphere, then all the reflected rays are concentrated in one spot; when the knife-edge is moved, the mirror darkens evenly all over, without any moving shadow effects.

Suppose the mirror is not, however, a perfect sphere: what will be the result? Not all the rays will be concentrated at the same point; those from either the edge or the centre will come to a point or focus nearer to the mirror than the remaining rays. If the curve is more flat (less curved) in the centre than near the edge, the rays from the centre will come together further from the mirror than the rays from the edge; the converse will be the case if the curve is deeper in the centre than near the edge.

The parabola, the form towards which we are striving, is deeper in the centre than is a sphere. Consequently, not all the rays of light will come together at the pinhole. Those from the centre will come to a focus a little nearer to the mirror than those from the edge. The exact amount of this difference depends upon the ratio of focal length to the diameter or aperture, and is given by the simple formula $\frac{r^2}{R}$, in which r is the radius of the zone tested and R is the radius of curvature of the mirror.

A practical example may be of help. For a mirror of 6 inches diameter and 48 inches focus, the radius of the edge is obviously 3 inches, and the radius of curvature (R) is twice the focus (48 inches), or 96 inches. Therefore when tested at the radius of curvature, the rays from the centre will come to a focus

$$\frac{r^2}{R} = \frac{9}{96} = \frac{3}{32}$$

inch nearer to the mirror than the rays from the edge. Hence if we adjust the knife-edge so that when it slides across, the edge darkens evenly all round, we should have to push it back $\frac{3}{32}$ inch before the centre also would darken evenly. If the amount actually necessary is less than this, the mirror form is intermediate between a sphere and a parabola, so that a little more polishing in the centre is required; if the amount is more than $\frac{3}{32}$ inch, the curve is too deep, and is what is known as a "hyperbola."

It is much better to leave the curve a little under the parabola (that is, not quite deep enough) than to make it a hyperbola (that is, too deep). The reason for this is that under-corrected mirrors often give excellent views; moreover, when the telescope is being used at night the temperature is usually falling, and very often the thick plate glass cannot keep pace with it, so that the slightly under-corrected curve temporarily becomes a full parabola. Under the same conditions an over-corrected or hyperbolic mirror would become still worse, and stars would appear to be surrounded by mist or haze. Either make the mirror a full parabola, or leave it slightly under—in the case of our 6-inch instrument, say $1/64$ inch less than the $3/32$ inch.

Possibly our first curve will be badly under-corrected, and want deepening. This can be done either by polishing with longer strokes, or by cutting away part of the pitch squares near the edge of the tool, so that the squares near the centre will do most of the polishing. If the curve is already too deep, we must do the reverse, using a short stroke and cutting away the squares near the centre of the tool. A little care and experience will demonstrate how the trimming of the tool will alter the nature of the curve.

When we are satisfied that the curve deepens in a regular manner from the edge to the centre, and also that it approximates to a parabola, we may try a star test—provided that the tube has been made and fitted with the diagonal and eyepiece attachments. At the focus, the image of a star should be a minute point of light which will expand into a disk when the eyepiece is pushed inside or drawn outside the focus. At equal distances inside and outside the focus, the disk of the expanded star image should look exactly the same. If the edge of the disk is sharp outside the focus but hazy with the eyepiece inside, the mirror is a hyperbola—that is to say, the curve is too deep in the centre; if the converse is the case, the mirror is almost spherical, and the curve must be deepened in the centre.

A very common defect is a "turned edge." This means

that all around the edge and perhaps for a quarter of an inch within, the curve has been flattened, so that this part of the curve has a long focus. A turned edge will impart a hazy or hairy fringe to the image of a star or planet. To find out whether the edge is turned, all we have to do is remove the knife-edge and substitute for it a low-power eyepiece. The lamp and the eyepiece should be mounted on the same support, so that they can be moved simultaneously towards or away from the mirror. At the exact radius of curvature, the image of the pinhole should be sharply defined. Now move the lamp and eyepiece towards the mirror. The image of the pinhole expands; if the edge remains sharp, the curve is true to the extreme edge, but if the edge of the enlarged pinhole image becomes hazy the mirror curve is flattened or turned down towards the edge. To rectify this, the mirror should be returned to the tool, and very short strokes used. When the turned edge is corrected for, the curve may have reverted to that of a sphere, and trimming of the tool will then be necessary to produce a parabola.

The mirror should now be carefully inspected to make sure that the bevel around the edge has not been ground away. If it has been, it must be restored. This done, the greatest care should be taken of the optical curve, and nothing sharp should be allowed to touch the mirror. It is the outcome of many hours of work, during which time every precaution has been taken to exclude dust or anything else which might prove harmful; and the mirror is the essential part of the instrument. When finally completed, it is ready to receive the actual reflecting surface, a thin film of either silver or aluminum. If the latter is preferred, the mirror must be sent to one of the firms specializing in this work, but silvering can be done at home.

Assuming that the mirror is to be home-silvered, the first thing to do is to clean it. If really dirty, as may easily be the case, it must first be washed with soap and water to remove the worst of the dirt; it is then ready to be made clean chemically. Place the mirror face-upwards, and then make a mop by taking a piece of cotton and tying it on to a stick. A little concentrated nitric acid * is poured on to the surface of the mirror, and is then spread all over the surface by means of the mop. Make sure that the edge is thoroughly clean; this will be shown by prismatic colours appearing as it dries. Go over the mirror several times, and take care that the corrosive acid does not come into contact with the skin or clothes. Swill the surface very thoroughly, and then place the mirror face downwards in a basin of water. Ensure that no air-bubbles are trapped under the curve; the way to avoid this is to lower the mirror edgeways into the water-bath.

To silver our 6-inch mirror, we require the following inexpensive chemicals: ⅛ oz. silver nitrate ($AgNO_3$); 1 oz. ammonia .880—a 10% solution; ¼ oz. pure caustic soda ($NaOH$); 1 oz. dextrose. The mirror should be silvered in a glass dish, suspended just clear of the sides with about an inch clear space between the mirror and the bottom of the dish; alternatively, it may be rested on the side of a tapering dish of slightly less diameter.

The given quantities are quite sufficient for our 6-inch mirror, and provided that care is taken there should be no

* It cannot be too strongly stressed that concentrated nitric acid is extremely dangerous stuff, and must be handled with great care.

difficulty in producing a satisfactory film. Use either distilled water or clean rainwater, unless your domestic supply of water is very soft.

Mix the ⅛ oz. of silver nitrate in 2 oz. water; set a little to one side in case of accidents, and add to the bulk the 10% solution of ammonia—drop by drop, and stirring well. At first a thick brownish mass will appear, but as the ammonia is added this begins to thin out. Stop the process when the mixture has become a little cloudy. In a separate glass mix ⅛ oz. of caustic soda with 2 oz. of water; pour into the ammoniated solution of silver nitrate, and stir very thoroughly. Add ammonia drop by drop, stirring constantly until it just clears. Pour in the remainder of the silver nitrate, thus restoring the cloudy appearance. Pour into the silvering dish. Make up a strong solution of dextrose in water (in the proportion of 1 in 10 parts), pour in the dish, and stir. There must be sufficient liquid in the dish to cover the face of the mirror and extend slightly up the sides. Lower the mirror, making sure that no air-bubbles have been trapped, and rock the dish gently from side to side.

With temperatures of around 60°F., silvering will be completed in from 10 to 15 minutes. Flakes of silver float on the liquid around the edge, and the film deposited on the mirror can be seen forming through the back. Lift off and examine; if the film is thin, replace the mirror at once. When the process is complete, lift the mirror out, swill it under a tap and set it on edge to dry. On no account touch the film with anything until it has dried very completely.

If the mirror was taken out at the correct moment, it will be found to have an even, brilliant film which will require no polishing. Should a whitish film appear, it may be polished by going over it lightly with a pad of cotton charged with a mere trace of fine rouge. When polished, the mirror is ready for use; a smart blow will dislodge the handle, the pitch can be scraped off, and the mirror can be placed in its cell ready for the telescope.

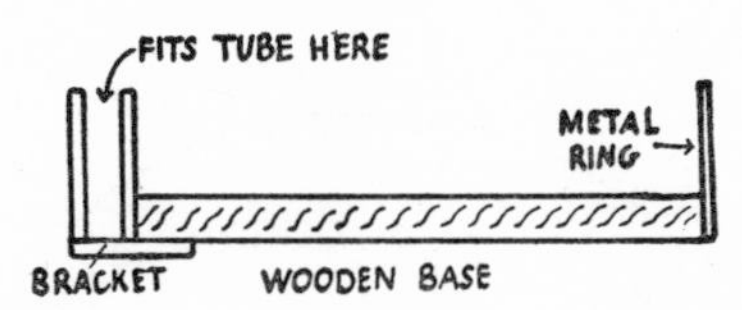

Fig. 9. Mirror cell—section with bracket

Meanwhile, the tube has been made. A single sheet of zinc or iron, measuring 21 inches by 48 inches, can be bent to form a rigid tube, the joint being secured by welding, soldering, or the drilling of holes to take very short bolts. When finished, the tube should be 48 inches long and 6½ inches in diameter (to allow for the thickness of the cell).

The cell to hold the mirror is easily made. It resembles a cake-tin; the outside diameter must be such that the cell can be slid into the tube, while the internal diameter must be a little larger than that of the mirror, so that a layer of felt, lino, cardboard or some similar substance can be inserted for the mirror edge to press against. The back of the cell should be of stout material; if metal, the thickness should be about ¼ inch, and if wood about one inch. It is necessary to make it thick because not only must it bear the weight of the mirror, but three screws must be introduced into tapped holes to allow for adjusting the mirror when it is inside the tube. A very simple cell can be constructed as follows. Prepare a wooden disk of the required diameter, and around it slip a metal ring sufficiently wide to protrude about 2 inches above the base; this ring can be a strip of tube material bent round, or alternatively made of brass with a soldered joint or even brazed. The strip is secured to the base by screws. The completed cell slips into the tube, and can be secured in position by three little brackets, as shown (Fig. 10).

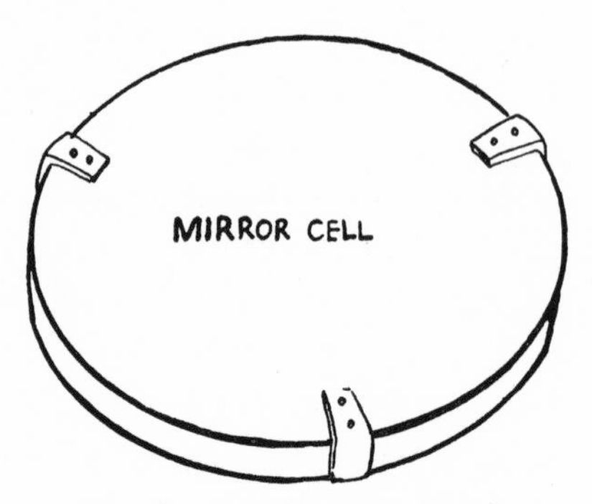

Fig. 10. Mirror cell—back

The eyepiece tube must now be fitted. First, we measure the distance from the face of the mirror to the open end of the tube. If the focus is exactly 48 inches, we must cut a hole in the tube at a distance from the mirror equal to the focus minus half the diameter of the tube and an inch or so more. If the mirror face is 2 inches from the closed or cell end of the tube, the distance of the mirror from the open end will be 46 inches. The tube is 6½ inches in diameter; half of this is 3¼ inches. Adding an inch, thus making 4¼ inches in all, then the centre of the eyepiece hole must be 2¼ inches from the open end, and thus 4¼ inches from the focus, which is clearly 2 inches beyond the open end.

When the diagonal mirror is in position, the focus will be 1 inch beyond the side of the tube.

The eyepiece hole should be 1$\frac{5}{16}$ in. in diameter, nicely rounded with a half-round file; it is made of a short piece of brass tubing of 1¼ inches internal diameter, tightly fitted, and if possible soldered in position nice and square to the main tube. The eyepiece itself is a push-in fit into another short piece of tubing, which slides into the fixed tube for focusing purposes.

In order to divert the rays from the great mirror into the eyepiece tube, we can use either a small plane mirror fixed at an angle of 45°, or a right-angled prism. If a plane mirror is used, it must be silvered in the same way as the great mirror; a prism requires no silvering. To hold a prism in place, it should be mounted in a metal grip as shown (Fig. 11) and rested on the ends of three metal screws pass-

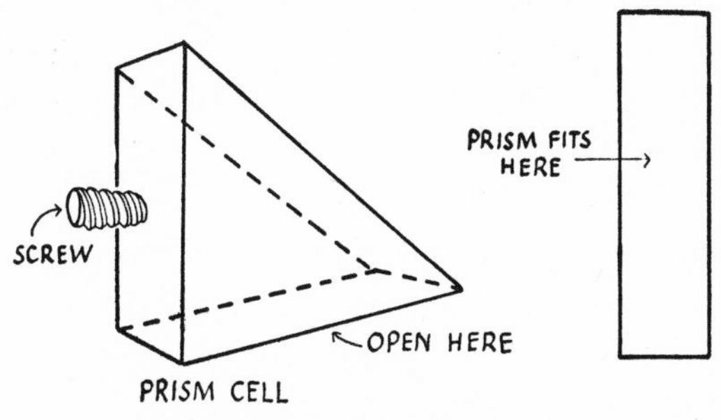

Fig. 11. Flat mount

ing through tapped holes in a disk a little over 1 inch in diameter, which is itself mounted on a single short arm which can be bolted to the tube. The centre of the prism must be in the centre of the tube and directly opposite to the centre of the eyepiece tube. The three screws allow for adjustment so that it can be squared on.

If a plane mirror is preferred, it had better be bought, as a true plane is much more difficult to produce than a true curve. The mirror will be elliptical, with a minor axis of about 1¼ inches; when in place it looks circular, because it is inclined at an angle of 45°. In the absence of a lathe, a plane mirror or "flat" may be cut out of thick plate glass, but few pieces of plate glass are truly plane, and it will be necessary to test the surface before cutting.

One way to do this is to lay the plate glass on a convenient table in the open air, and observe the reflected image of a star or the Moon with the aid of a small telescope previously focused for direct vision. If the mirror is truly flat, the reflected image will be as sharp as in the direct view, and in the same focus. If on the other hand the glass is concave or convex, the image may still be good, but the telescope will have to be adjusted. If the eyepiece has to be moved in towards the objective, the mirror is concave; if we have to rack out, the mirror is convex, while if the image is distorted the mirror is useless. In this way we can select a suitable piece of glass and cut the flat out of it, carefully smoothing and bevelling the edge. The flat will be inserted in a small piece of tube cut off at an angle of 45°. A disk of brass is soldered at the flat end, and a threaded rod is fixed to it, so that it can be mounted against the fixed disk—which is mounted on the supporting bracket. The threaded rod passes through a clewing hole in the disk, and is secured by a nut. The disk itself rests upon the three adjusting screws already mentioned.

A cover like a saucepan lid should be made to fit the

open end of the main telescope tube, to exclude dust—and also sulphur and moisture, which otherwise would quickly tarnish the main mirror. It is also advisable to make a very light cover for the flat, when the telescope is not in use. For this purpose, thin sheet brass is excellent; the cover should take the form of a short cylinder cut off at an angle of 45°, and must fit very easily over the cell.

When completed, the inside of the main tube should be blackened to avoid reflections which might otherwise introduce "ghosts" into the field of view. The outside of the tube should be painted; a light grey or aluminum is best, although some reflectors are painted white. A handle should be fitted to the tube for convenience in carrying.

The adjustment of the optical system is very important—if the mirrors are not correctly positioned, the resulting image will be faulty. First remove the eyepiece, and look through the eyepiece tube. The flat will be seen, in the centre of which should appear the main mirror. The image of the main mirror should be a uniform circle of light. If the mirror is not square with the main tube, however, this will not be the case, and the end of the tube itself will be seen on one side. This means that the main mirror is tilted in the tube, and must be squared on by screwing in the adjusting screw on the side where the end of the tube appears.

When in correct adjustment, the main mirror should appear as a circle of light in the centre of the flat, and the flat itself should be seen reflected in the centre of the main mirror; everything should be symmetrical. If the mirror is a true parabola, the eyepiece should come sharply to a focus, so that the slightest motion in or out will be obvious.

The focus should be critically sharp in one position only.

As the reflector itself is perfectly achromatic, any false color around the edge of a bright object must be due to the lack of achromatism of the eyepiece. If the field of view is not uniformly illuminated, either the flat is too small to transmit all the rays from the great mirror, or the eyepiece or eyepiece tube is not at right angles to the main tube and the optical axis of the mirrors. A small flat will serve for high powers, but for low powers, when the field of view is large, there will be a falling-off of light all round the edge of the field. A flat of the size recommended (1¼ in.) will obstruct only 1/25 of the total light of the mirror, an amount which can be entirely disregarded. On no account try tilting the great mirror with the eyepiece at the side of the tube, as in the Herschelian arrangement. This is bound to distort the image, and will also give a lateral reflection (east and west being transposed), which is a nuisance when comparing the telescopic view obtained with a map or chart.

In order to protect the film, we must make provision to cover up the main mirror when it is not in use. Large instruments have a door in the tube near the mirror end, through which the cover can be inserted or removed. This cover usually takes the form of a lid, again resembling that of a saucepan, within which is a pad of cotton batting which can be pressed firmly on to the mirror. This pad is often made of fine wash-leather stuffed with cotton; and it should sometimes be exposed to bright sunshine or to a fire to make sure that it is absolutely dry. Protected in this way, the mirror will remain bright for years.

For small reflectors, the cylindrical sheet tube is the

easiest to make; it also gives the greatest protection, costs the least, and looks the best. If preferred, however, a square wooden tube can be used. This form also is very easy to make, and performs well owing to the fact that wood is a virtual non-conductor of heat. On the other hand it is much heavier, because the sides must have a thickness of at least half an inch, and it is also liable to warp, so that the adjustments are more open to disarrangement than is the case with a metal tube. Tube currents, which become troublesome with large instruments, will rarely affect the popular 6-inch size, and it is only upon occasions when the air temperature is subject to frequent fluctuations that they will be noticed at all.

Should the telescope-maker lack enough facilities to make the various parts exactly as described above, he can improvise. In the absence of metal-working tools, including taps, the flat or plane mirror could be attached to the supporting bracket without adjusting screws, the bracket itself being capable of a slight movement along the axis of the tube and also from side to side, the correct position being found before the insertion of the bolts or screws. If the mirror is not truly parabolic, and the maker's skill is insufficient to make it so, it may still be serviceable, the defective zone (especially if around the edge) being blocked out by a stop. Perhaps there will be no facilities for cutting out an ellipse; in this case the flat must be a square or oblong piece of glass. Such a flat will perform quite well provided that its surface is true; it merely requires fitting to a suitable cell, and silvering on its face. Do not use a piece of looking-glass. Such a glass is rarely flat; and since it is silvered at the back, there will be several reflections, with the result that what should be a single star will look merely the brightest of many!

The telescope completed, we are now faced with the problem of mounting it upon a stand or support of some kind. This matter is so important that it merits a separate chapter. Meanwhile, a few final words of advice may be given. Do not (1) begin to fine-grind before the coarse grinding has brought the curve to the required radius; (2) begin polishing before the fine grinding is complete and the disk is semi-transparent; (3) attempt to silver unless the mirror is chemically clean; (4) forget to bevel the edge; or (5) forget to keep the mirror covered up when not in use.

Remember, success depends upon the careful observance of the minor details.

IV

FITTING UP THE TELESCOPE

ANYONE who is handy with his hands will probably want to make a better kind of stand than that which we have already described—a really sound engineering job, which will stand up to hard work and remain in good condition for a much longer period than a simple home-made mount. The principle of construction is the same, but the material used is metal, and a lathe is almost a necessity.

Before describing the making of various types of stands, either of altazimuth or equatorial form, we must spare a moment for that hoary and fearful contrivance known as the pillar-and-claw. This is a beautifully finished affair, generally gold-lacquered, consisting of three curved legs joining into a round base into which screws a tapering pillar—to the top of which a short cradle is attached by a "knuckle joint." The legs fold up when not in use, and the pillar, or part of it, is capable of rotation to allow for motion in azimuth. The telescope is secured to the cradle, and can be directed to any altitude by means of the knuckle joint. The pillar-and-claw stand is commonly supplied with small refractors; indeed, some makers of instruments do not appear to have heard of any other type of mounting!

While this affair is better than no stand at all, and may

be of service if there is a convenient post or similar support to hand, it is not favoured by the practical observer, for it has many defects. The telescope is not balanced, and will slowly "creep" in altitude unless the knuckle joint is screwed up tightly, in which case it is too stiff to allow the instrument to move easily. The pillar lacks rigidity, and either rotates too easily, accompanied by shake, or too stiffly, so that considerable force is required to move it at all. Sometimes a vertical steadying-rod is fitted between the eye-end of the telescope and the pillar. This conceals the want of balance, and allows for easier adjustment in altitude. A small worm and worm-wheel is occasionally fitted at the base of the pillar, and at first is very stiff, but rapidly wears, and soon produces a great deal of backlash. A pillar-and-claw stand is ideal for a telescope which is never used, permanently locked away in its case or standing in a library, but it should never be seen in the hands of the serious amateur.

For a small refractor, the best stand is the so-called garden tripod, which consists of three legs, each formed of two pieces of wood about 5 feet long, stayed at intervals, and tapering towards the bottom. The upper part of the stand, like the legs, is best made of mahogany or oak, and consists of a block, two or three inches thick, with three projections—the whole being cut from the same flawless and seasoned piece of wood. Each projection is drilled so as to take a bolt, which acts as a pivot for a leg. When not in use, the tripod can be folded up so as to occupy as little room as possible; when wanted, the legs open out as desired. Sometimes a metal rod is fixed centrally in the block, protruding downwards. A sliding "spider" with three arms, jointed to the legs about halfway down, not only makes the tripod more rigid when extended but also limits the motion of the legs so that they all move by the same amount. Pieces of metal should be nailed or screwed to the bottoms of the legs, thus forming shoes to take the wear and protect the wood.

The portable tripod can be fitted either with an altazimuth or an equatorial head. If an altazimuth is required, it can be made from ¼-inch or ⅜-inch sheet brass, and consists of a rectangular plate with a hole in the centre, to which the uprights are secured by countersunk screws. The bottoms of the uprights are drilled with three tapping holes and tapped with screws. The plate is drilled with three clearing holes, countersunk on the underneath. A stay may be inserted between the uprights, and secured by six countersunk screws, two in each upright and two in the plate. The upper end of each upright is drilled ⅜ of an inch, and screwed down to the hole to make a slot. The telescope is either drilled to take two short ⅜-inch bolts, inserted from within the tube and tightened by a thin locknut, or a collar is made to fit the tube tightly and two studs are screwed into it. In any case, the trunnions must be placed as near the balancing point as possible. Nuts prevent too free a motion. A steadying-rod and slow motions can be fitted afterwards, if desired. The fork will rotate round a ½-inch bolt protruding through the centre of the tripod block; if a stretcher or spider stay is used for the legs, it may be the upper part of this. The fork should not be in contact with the wooden block, but with a metal plate secured to the block by wood screws (which must have countersunk heads).

If an equatorial head is required, a great deal more work will be involved, though the final result will, of course, be vastly superior. The fork will be replaced by two components A and B (Fig. 12). A is a metal plate having a short

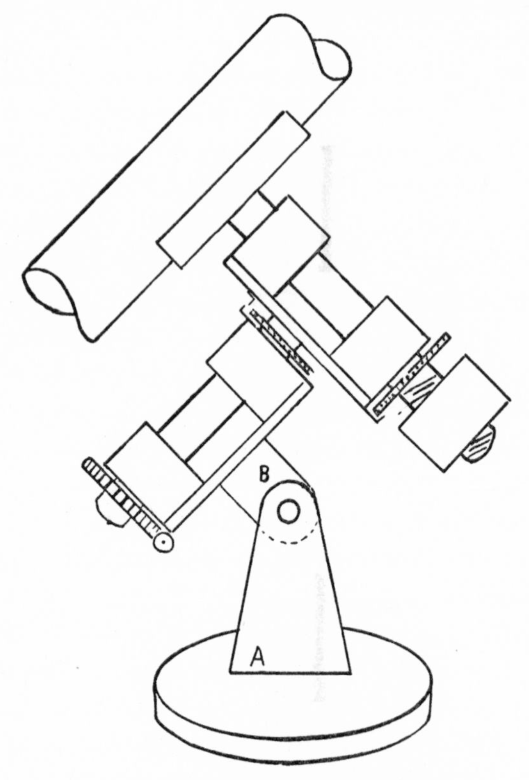

Fig. 12. Equatorial stand

upright of at least ¾-inch thickness, drilled with ½-inch clearance at the top, the metal being filed concentric with the hole. A is rigidly fixed to the tripod wooden block. B consists of a fork, milled from the solid, or fabricated to fit nicely over the upright in A. The fork is drilled ½ inch, and a fitted bolt passed through. The best method would be a turned steel rod, threaded ½ inch at either end, and fitting the hole in the middle. Two large round nuts are turned, drilled critically, and tapped ½ inch. These should be milled on the rim. When assembled, the nuts will tighten the fork on the upright and allow for change in latitude.

The fork carries a brass plate about 6 inches long and 2 inches wide, cut from ⅜-inch or ½-inch plate. Two plummer blocks can be purchased and secured to the plate at either end, or the bearings used be made from the solid, split, the screwing bolts inserted and then drilled ¾ inch to take the polar axis, which can be made from ¾-inch bright steel rod, threaded at either end but for a longer distance at the lower end.

A similar plate complete with plummer blocks and rod is now made, drilled, and tapped ¾ inch in the centre, and the polar axis screwed tightly into it. This second plate is for the setting in declination. To one end of the rod is fitted a cradle to take the telescope; this is made from thick metal hollowed out on one side with a radius equal to that of the telescope tube. It also might be made from a metal plate to which is fastened a wooden cradle shaped to fit the tube, which is secured by hinged brass bands or even leather straps. The other end of the rod carries the balance weight, which is made from one or more solid pieces of iron bar drilled centrally and tapped so as to permit adjustment for perfect balancing.

The polar axis may be fitted with worm and wheel, the wheel being keyed to the shaft but the worm in its cage being pivoted at one end so as to allow for disengaging from the wheel when a quick motion is required. When in gear, it is secured either by a spring or by a rod passing through clearing holes in the worm cage and bracket.

Circles can be fitted to both the polar and declination axes. That on the polar axis will indicate right ascension (R.A.), while the other will of course indicate declination (Decl.). If the reader has a lathe and also a dividing head, the circles may be made from ¼ inch brass sheet, turned 4 inches diameter, and drilled centrally ¾ inch. Set up on a mandrel between centres, and by using the dividing head scribe deeply 360 equally spaced lines around the circumference, and, more lightly, two lines from the centre of the disk to one edge, equally spaced between the main divisions. At intervals of 5 degrees stamp counterclockwise 0 to 360, or 0 to 24 at intervals of 15 lines, according to whether it is desired to calibrate in degrees or hours. Probably hours will be more suitable.

A similar disk should be made scribed with one line and stamped 0. This disk will be fixed in position; the divided disk comes against this, but can be rotated—it is fixed to the shaft (Fig. 13). To set the telescope in R.A., we first note the sidereal time, and then turn the divided disk under the fixed pointer attached to the bearing, until we have set the indicated time. The polar axis is then rotated until the single-lined disk reads the R.A. of the star against the divided disk.

The declination circle is also 4 inches in diameter, turned, drilled, and tapped to fit the declination axis. It is divided into 360 degrees, and again subdivided and then stamped 0 degrees to 90 degrees, back again to 0 degrees, in each quadrant. A fixed pointer is secured to the bearing, and the circle when assembled should be fitted so as to read 0 degrees when the telescope is pointed to the celestial equator, or 90 degrees when pointed to the pole. It is then keyed in position, or secured by a setscrew or taper pin.

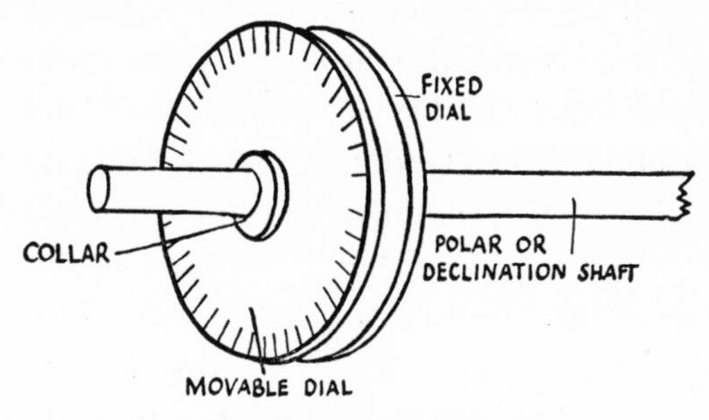

Fig. 13. Dials fixing

Verniers can be fitted if desired in order to increase the accuracy of the settings, but can readily be dispensed with. After dividing, the circles should be heated on the hot plate and gold-lacquered. The plates may be black-lacquered if of brass, but all brass nuts and collars should be gold-lacquered.

If the telescope is fitted with a worm drive, we have a choice between hand operation and clock drive. Hand motion may be given by a long handle with a knob at the end, but a clock drive is much more difficult to construct, though it does vastly increase the pleasure of observing.

One of the easiest clock-drives is provided by a synchronous electric motor, fitted with reduction gear so as to rotate the polar axis once every 23 hours 56 minutes. If the reader lives in a district without electric supply, however, some other method will have to be adopted, and in such a case it might be advisable to construct a sand clock.

The principle of this is easy to grasp. We have a long tube containing sand, which can escape at any desired rate by means of an adjustable aperture or tap. A heavy weight fits easily within the tube, which is set vertically. As the sand escapes, the weight descends, and imparts its motion by a cord wound round a drum to which is attached reduction gearing (Fig. 14). The chief drawback of such an arrangement is the tendency to stick in damp weather, and there is also the labour of winding up the weight and returning the sand when the device has run down. Naturally, a sand clock weighs a good deal, and is therefore better suited for a fixed than for a portable instrument. If carefully made, however, it will work very well—and it is cheap.

The long tube may be anything—even a drainpipe could be pressed into service at a pinch! It should be in two portions, fitting on each other. The lower portion does not take the weight; this is ensured by a metal stand upon which the upper sand-filled section is placed. The lower tube is merely to receive the exhaust sand. If the tubes are of the same size, we can interchange at will. When the upper part is empty and the lower full, we can merely change them round, and the drive continues. Such a device will drive the instrument for a couple of hours at a time, the correct speed being controlled by the tap. The tap itself should be fitted at the bottom of a slightly larger tube, which is fixed to the stand and into which the other tube fits—thus preventing any sand being lost or blown onto the other parts of the telescope.

For a reflector, the stand must be modified, because the

eyepiece is at the top of the tube and it is advantageous to keep everything as low as possible. The tube may be placed in an open or a closed fork; or it may be mounted

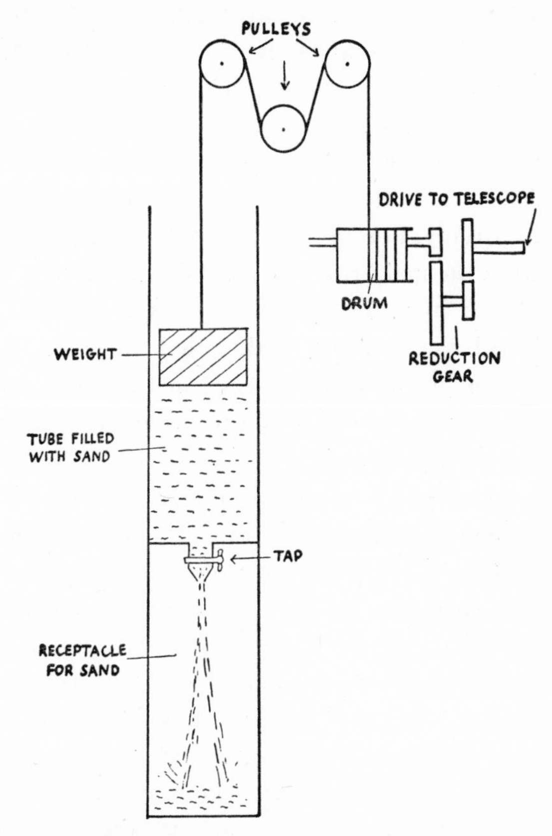

Fig. 14. Sand clock or clepsydra

on a declination axis, as in the case of a refractor. If the closed fork is desired, it can take the form of an oblong wooden frame made from 3-inch by 2-inch timber, and long enough for the tube to swing inside. The tube turns on trunnions, and a rod at either end of the long fork is constrained by bearings. If we adopt the system of two axes, as with a refractor, all we have to do is to make everything very solid. In all other respects, the fitting of the circles and other refinements is precisely similar.

If a lathe is available, metal tubes should be used in the case of a refractor. Turn a collar to fit the tube tightly, knurl the raised edge and bore to fit the eyepiece draw-tube. We can also turn a cell for the object-glass from thick brass tubing. Bore to the required diameter, and turn outside to fit the main tube. Thread the lower part inside, 50 threads per inch. The objective rests at the inner end of this thread, against a step; a threaded collar can then be fitted so as to just grip the lenses when screwed in. The lenses should be allowed slight movement, and on no account be tightly nipped.

A rack and pinion for focusing is an advantage over the simple push-pull arrangement, but can be made only by a skilled mechanic, for which reason it is best to purchase it. If it is to be made, the rack itself can either be bought or else milled in the lathe; alternatively, both rack and pinion could be hobbed. The rack should be silver-soldered to the rack tube, and must be absolutely parallel to it. The pinion, pinion-shaft and bearings are secured to the outer tube, which is fitted with a good bearing collar in which the rack tube slides. The rack itself is cleared by a slot. The tube of a rack-and-pinion focusing adjustment should not be less than 1¼ inches in diameter; this will be found the minimum required to accommodate the standard 1¼-inch-diameter eyepiece tube. All things considered, it is well worth purchasing a rack and pinion—only, do not obtain one which has too coarse a feed. To rack out the tube an inch, the pinion shaft and knurled head should have to make at least three turns, and more are desirable.

If the completed arrangement is of the equatorial type, we must adjust it correctly; only a truly oriented stand will follow a celestial object faithfully. First of all, the polar axis must be set accurately in the meridian. From an almanac, find the time when the Pole Star is at its upper culmination (that is, directly above the true polar point), and then turn the telescope so that the Pole Star is in the centre of the field of view. The tube is then pointing in the plane of the meridian, and we may set the polar axis to point in the same direction. However, the telescope is not at the same angle as that of the latitude of the place of observation, because the Pole Star does not exactly mark the true pole—in other words, the telescope and the polar axis are not parallel. With a low-power eyepiece, the Pole Star and the true pole will be in the same field. It is true that the pole is not marked in any way, but by directing the telescope so that when at its upper culmination the Pole Star is near the lower edge of the field of view, it will be possible to note the dimensions of the circle which the star describes around the pole—and so to adjust the instrument so that when the centre of its motion (that is, the true pole) is in the centre of the field, the tube and the polar axis are parallel.

If the polar axis is not set truly in the plane of the meridian, it will be found that a star will drift slowly out of the field of view when the telescope is driven. If the star drifts towards the north (the lower part of the ordinary inverting eyepiece), the polar axis is pointing towards the west; if the star drifts to the south, the axis is pointing to the east of the true meridian.

We must in any case expect such a drift in the case of the Moon, because the Moon has a comparatively rapid motion of its own in both right ascension and declination. Hence, adjustments must be made at intervals. The motion in declination is most marked when the Moon is near one of the nodes of its orbit (that is, the points of intersection of the plane of its orbit with that of the Earth). A hand-operated slow motion in declination is an advantage, and can take the form of a worm and wheel attached to the declination axis with the means for disconnecting when required. Alternatively, it may be a friction drive; this latter can be made by turning a disk of suitable diameter, drilling, and keying to the declination shaft, afterwards fixing a rubber band around the edge. A long handle, carrying a small disk and with a Hooke's joint, has its bearing pivoted to the declination housing; the disk can thus be brought into contact with the rubber-edged disk as required. A similar device can be applied to the polar axis for driving a small telescope. Rubber-edged disks can be adapted from toy cycles, prams, or scooters!

(When making these somewhat elaborate stands, it is just as well to prepare also a very simple piece of apparatus—merely a round rod, such as a broom-handle, with one end pointed and the other cut off square. Quite useful observations can be made with a pair of binoculars, and it will be found that by sitting on a chair with the rod lightly held between the legs, the pointed end on the ground, the binoculars can be kept steady merely by resting them on the upper end of the rod. Simple as this device appears, it is a great boon for that delightful occupation—sweeping the skies with a very low power.)

It must always be remembered that most astronomical work is done at night. Having a fine instrument is all very well, but it can become a dangerous weapon in the dark. Also, we must have a light to read the circles; and although one can always carry a flashlight, it is better and more satisfactory to have a couple of lamps in holders fixed to the stand, current being drawn from a battery and controlled by a switch. The lamps should be so placed as to illuminate the circles; they can also be used for reading maps and making drawings.

Very often, something will be found lying around which simply invites being incorporated into the stand. It may be part of an old sewing machine, or rods and wheels from an old cycle. Neither must ordinary piping be overlooked, as it often forms a convenient bearing for the shafts. Equatorial stands have been made from two pieces of tubing welded together so as to form a T, the larger piece of tube becoming the polar axis and being fitted in bearings, the shorter piece acting as a bearing for the declination axis. A stout pipe fixed upright in concrete will serve as a rigid support, and the various heads can be fixed to it if the pipe is also filled with concrete and a long bolt inserted with a few threads projecting above the end. When the concrete sets, the bolt is firmly gripped, and all we want is a nut to clamp the head to the pillar.

It is better to make a stand too massive rather than construct one of the slender, flexible and wind-shaken devices so often seen. Little satisfaction will be had if the object under examination merely dances about. Care must also be taken with the eyepiece tube—or it will tend to slide when the telescope is set at certain inclinations, so that the focus is continually being lost.

With a reflector mounted as an altazimuth, the eyepiece is always horizontal, but if mounted as an equatorial the eyepiece will assume awkward inclinations, the observer having sometimes to grovel on his knees and at others to bend right over the tube. To obviate this, some reflectors are not mounted directly to the declination axis, but can rotate within a ring which is attached to the axis. In other arrangements the upper segment of the tube can be rotated, and with it the flat and eyepiece. Without some rotative capability of the instrument, the observer must be prepared to "do the bends."

A word must be said about one or two special forms of mountings devised for the convenience of the observer. Such is the polar mounting, in which the tube itself is fixed at an angle equal to that of the latitude, the mirror being at the top. A plane mirror mounted on an axis and suitably driven reflects the light from the object up the tube. With this arrangement, the eyepiece remains in a fixed position. Another method is to replace the Newtonian flat by a convex mirror, thus making the telescope a Cassegrain, and fixing a small flat mirror directly opposite one of the trunnions, which is tubular and acts as the eyepiece tube. James Nasmyth, co-author of a well-known book on the Moon (and, incidentally, inventor of the steam hammer), mounted his 20-inch reflector in this manner, the whole instrument being fixed to a large turntable so that it could easily be rotated. The mounting of this instrument is now on view at the Science Museum in South Kensington.

The Coudé principle has been adapted to reflectors. In some instances the tube is horizontal and in the meridian, light being reflected by a plane mirror pierced by a central hole through which the rays pass before reaching the eyepiece. The difficulty here is the plane mirror, which must be considerably larger than the main mirror and also perfectly flat. Such a mirror would cost more than the telescope itself, so that this arrangement is rarely seen. There is also loss of light owing to the introduction of an extra reflecting surface, and in general the Coudé principle is more readily adapted to refractors than to reflectors.

The best performance will be obtained with a good mirror mounted as a Newtonian, the tubes being rigid and supported on a stand fixed out doors. In the absence of an observatory properly so called, the instrument may be covered with a tarpaulin or some other waterproof covering. If the tube is really water-tight, it may be left in the open without other protection. Moore's 12½-inch is protected by a simple shed, run off on rails when the telescope is to be used; Wilkins' 15¼-inch has stood in the open for five years without any damage without requiring any attention other than repainting. Repainting would, however, be required whether the instrument were covered or not.

V

SOME REFINEMENTS

ONE OF the most annoying experiences which can happen to the owner of a telescope is to see some star or planet shining brightly in the sky, and yet be quite unable to get it into the field of view. With a reflector one can always squint along the tube, but frequently this does not have the desired effect, and a Newtonian reflector has its eyepiece to one side, so that looking up the tube generally leads nowhere, as by the time one has scrambled back to the eyepiece the object is already out of view.

The simplest remedy for this time-wasting and soul-vexing operation is the addition of a *finder*. This is a small telescope, a mere spyglass, fitted with a low-power eyepiece, and having therefore a large field of view. The eyepiece is usually fitted with cross wires or some other means of locating the centre of the field, and both object glass and eyepiece are capable of being adjusted for focusing purposes.

The finder is mounted on the large telescope parallel to the main tube—not of course directly upon it, or the eye could not be brought near enough to look through it, but supported by brackets. It should be possible to adjust the finder easily without using either a spanner or a screwdriver, though it must be admitted that many finders are so mounted that it is virtually impossible to adjust them at all.

There is only one sensible way to mount a finder. Make two rings, a little larger internally than the diameter of the finder, so that the finder itself can be held at the points of three screws passing through the rings. The rings are held away from the main tube by a short bracket. At a pinch, these rings might be made from old curtain rings pierced by three holes spaced 120° apart. The screws pass through these holes. A better way is to turn up brass rings, 3/16 or 1/4 inch thick and 1/4 inch wide, drilled and tapped and fitted with knurled, headed screws. The rings should be drilled and tapped for the threaded stem of the mounting bracket.

If the internal diameter of the ring is about 3/8 inch larger than the finder, there will be plenty of space for setting the finder accurately parallel to the main tube, provided that the brackets are set reasonably in line and along the axis of the tube. The knurled heads allow the screws to be adjusted with the fingers.

The finder itself is easily made, and requires no description after our previous instructions for making a simple refractor, except that the length must be kept down. If a toy telescope can be obtained, all the better; any low power will serve. Sometimes sights are used in place of a tube finder, but the trouble of making and fitting the proper thing is so slight as not to warrant any substitute.

A finder fitted to a refractor rarely requires any adjustment, but with a reflector conditions are different. If either of the main mirrors be moved, the finder will need adjustment. Since the mirrors do need occasional attention, the finder also must be altered in adjustment. To adjust a finder, bring some easily found object such as the Moon into the field of the main telescope, and adjust the finder so that the Moon appears central in its large field and low-power eyepiece (an extra refinement is to reckon from some prominent lunar feature, generally a known crater lying on or near the terminator). Having secured this rough adjustment, it will serve to bring some apparently slow-moving star, such as the Pole Star, into the centre of the main telescope field, when the finder also can be set with the star in the centre of the field of view. Once set, a finder will prove an invaluable guide and help in picking up objects, while its own individual merits will be appreciated should a really fine comet chance to appear.

Very large telescopes have finders which themselves are quite large by amateur standards. The 33-inch Meudon reflector has a 5-inch refractor as its finder, and the 36-inch Lick refractor has a 6-inch finder. These finders are themselves sufficiently large to require finders, so that we have in fact two finders mounted one upon the other.

A necessity for a refracting telescope, be it a main instrument or a finder, is a *dewcap*. If the object glass is situated at or very near the top of the tube, it will certainly become coated with moisture on damp nights. A simple remedy is a dewcap, which is merely a short length of tube blackened on the inside, and arranged to fit fairly tightly either to the outside of the object glass cell or to the main tube itself. It prevents, or at least seriously reduces, the risk of dewing, and often makes all the difference between a good night's work and an indifferent view. Although a simple tube will serve, it is an advantage to line it inside with some material such as black velvet or felt.

A great deal of pleasure, as well as results of lasting value, can be derived from the use of a *micrometer,* which is a device by means of which the apparent sizes, diameters, etc., of distant objects can be measured in seconds of arc, instead of merely estimated by the eye.

In order to measure the distance between two points—whether they are two marks on a piece of paper, two stars in the field of a telescope, two craters on the Moon or two points marking the diameter of a planet—something must move. In the case of two marks on paper we could, of course, use an ordinary ruler, but this would be rather difficult in the case of a celestial body such as a planet! Yet there must be movement of some sort, and this might be arranged in one of two ways. We could have some fixed point in the eyepiece—a wire, for instance—just touching the star, and keep the telescope stationary, noting the time interval elapsing before the second star also touched the wire. This apparent drift across the field when the telescope is fixed is not, of course, anything to do with the star itself, and is due merely to the rotation of the Earth, but it could be turned to some account.

In the second arrangement, the telescope is driven so as to counteract the rotation of the Earth, and consequently the two stars remain fixed in the field of view. We now have two wires. One is fixed, just touching the first star; the other wire is moved by means of a screw until it touches the second star. By noting the number of turns we have given the screw in order to move the second wire from one star to the other, it is possible to ascertain the distance between the two stars in seconds of arc.

The first method can be used with an altazimuth telescope if a reliable clock or watch is available, but the second method is independent of time, and is vastly superior. It does, however, need an equatorially mounted telescope, and there must be clock drive, unless a perfect following can be imparted by hand.

The moving-wire or linear micrometer is well within the capacity of the careful and skilled amateur worker, particularly if he is used to making models. The instrument consists essentially of a short piece of tubing made to fit the eyepiece tube, and having a flat plate fitted to the other end. This plate has a central hole, and is soldered to the brass tubing. V-shaped guides are secured to the plate by screws, and must be absolutely parallel to each other. Between these guides is fitted a U-shaped brass piece, the "legs" being bevelled to fit the guides (an easy sliding fit is desirable), while a screw fits into the short end, and is soldered. This screw passes through a clearing hole in a brass strip fixed to the main plate between and at the ends of the guides. A spiral spring between the end of the U-piece and the end strip would keep them apart, but the piece can be moved to and fro by a large knurled nut with a divided head. A flat plate bearing a short piece of tubing for the eyepiece is fixed to the first plate, so that the two pieces of tubing are in line; the head should be graduated into 5-degree divisions.

With a scriber, mark lines heavily across the guide plate and along a vertical diameter of the hole. A similar line must be scribed at right angles. Also scribe vertically across the U-piece, and near the ends of the "legs." Make a frame of light wire, catch a spider and place it on the frame. Now tap the frame lightly. The spider will (if co-operative!) lower itself by a single thread; as it does so, wind the thread on to the metal frame.* Place a little wax on the scribed lines, and, holding the wire frame, place the threads in the lines. Trim off. We now have two threads at right angles and one fixed, while the other is movable by rotating the knurled and divided head. Take a piece of machine screw and flatten on both sides. Fix this across the lower part of the hole, so as to be in focus together with the threads. The fixed vertical thread should pass through the roof of one of the flattened threads of the screw. The purpose of this is to show at a glance how many whole turns of the head have been given.

Having made the micrometer, the value of one rotation of the head in seconds of arc can be found by selecting two points whose distance apart is known. These two points may, for instance, be the two components of a double star. Placing one star so that it is concealed by the fixed vertical wire, and turning the instrument so as to place the fixed horizontal wire, or thread, parallel to the line joining the two stars, the head is rotated until the movable wire touches the second star. Knowing the distance between the stars, and the number of complete turns and fractions of a turn given, the value of one rotation can be found, and will be constant for that particular telescope or any other telescope of the same focal length (note this qualification, as it is often forgotten). It must be remembered that since the eyepiece must focus on the threads, it must be a positive eyepiece.

This instrument can be used well only with a clock-driven, equatorially mounted telescope, so that if this is not available we must have recourse to the *ring microm-*

* This method may sound most peculiar, but—strange to say—it really does work!

eter. This has no moving wires, and consists essentially of a ring placed at the focus of the eyepiece. The ring may be a wire circle suspended in the field of view, or may be etched upon a truly plane piece of glass. The telescope is fixed, and the two objects to be measured pass across the field of view—including the ring—and are timed in so doing. The value of the diameter of the ring in seconds of arc is found, and the time taken to traverse any chord is also found. The time will vary according to the declination of the object, being least with low declinations and greatest with high declinations (this is obvious enough; near the pole declination is high, and motion least evident). In a ring micrometer, time takes the place of the screw and divided head of the linear type.

Another type of instrument, known as the *differential* or *cross-bar micrometer,* will be found useful for lunar work. It consists of a plate with a hole of about ¾ inch diameter, and a short piece of tubing on either side. Across the hole are placed either threads or very fine wires, two at right angles and two others dividing the angles thus formed, so that the field of view is divided into eight equal sections. Here again we arrange the device so that the apparent motion of the two objects we wish to measure is parallel to one wire, and we note the difference of time with which the two objects cross the wires (one above the central point, the other below).

In making this instrument, it is important to see that the threads or wires are well stretched and truly spaced; great care is required when scribing the lines. Spider threads are finer and more uniform than wires, but are easily damaged. Wires can be soldered in place, but only just enough solder to ensure fixing should be used.

Another instrument which should prove of interest to the amateur is a device to indicate the amount of heat received from the Moon. It can only be used when the sky is absolutely clear, for even a thin haze will cut off the inconceivably small amount of heat of even the full moon. Before first quarter and again after last quarter the amount of heat is too small to be measured with this device.

It consists of a small horseshoe magnet, in the field of which is suspended a thermocouple made of two dissimilar metals, such as alumel and copper, or constantan and copper. In a couple found by Wilkins (who developed this instrument) to work well, the dimensions were: Length of couple, 0.5 inch; thickness of wires, 0.004 inch; distance apart, 0.005 inch; weight, 0.005 gram, suspension thickness, 0.005 inch.

The completed instrument is shown in Fig. 15. When the wires are set side by side in the field of view, the separation being 0.005 inch, it may be graduated in seconds of arc by timing the passage of a star near the equator (Delta Orionis is one such star). An altazimuth reflector should be used, as with this type of telescope the eyepiece will always be horizontal. It will be found that if the wires are first placed edge-on, and the couple is suspended so as to allow one end only to be exposed to radiation, the wires will turn when the light of the Moon falls on the end. They will also turn if radiation from any other source falls on them—and this includes heat from the observer's body; while if he happens to be smoking, and comes near the couple, it will probably make a complete rotation! Effective shading by some non-conductor, such as wood, is a necessity. The sketch (Fig. 15) is almost self-explanatory.

If the telescope is electrically driven, it is advantageous to have the controls conveniently at the eye end—indeed,

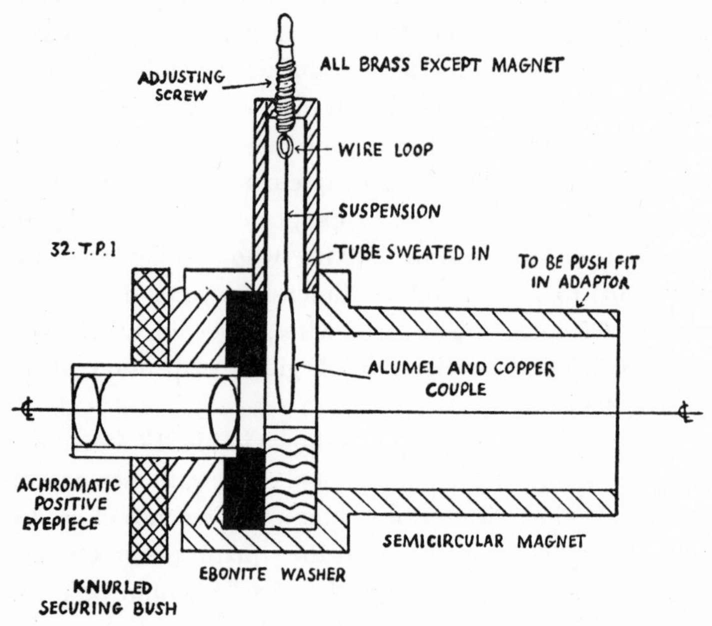

Fig. 15. Thermal eyepiece

the controls should always be made easily accessible. Large telescopes such as the Yerkes 40-inch and the Meudon 33-inch are so arranged, and the hand wheels for clamping and setting in right ascension and declination make an imposing show at the eye end.

Windy nights can be very trying. They often give good definition, but tend to shake the telescope. If the instrument is mounted in the open air, it will be found a great advantage to fix up a windscreen. This may be made of canvas fastened to poles, which can either be set up or arranged to drop into holes in the ground. Such a screen will break the force of the wind, and enable observations to be carried on which would be impossible otherwise owing to the quivering of the telescope. Such screens are often attached to the shutters of observatory domes, and can be run up and down as desired.

Eyepieces, micrometers, and other delicate instruments should be kept in a dry place. The ideal way is for each to have its own case or box, which will not only make the instrument easy to find but will also exclude dust. For eyepieces, a case may be made from cardboard tubes of suitable diameters; details of the contents should be marked on the outside.

The matters mentioned in this chapter may be "refinements" in the sense that they are not absolutely necessary; but they are certainly a great convenience, and since they can be made so easily they come almost into the category of necessities to the serious observer.

VI

EYEPIECES

A POOR eyepiece will spoil the performance of the best telescope ever made, and will be like using a good gramophone with a worn needle. There are also eyepieces which although optically good are unsuitable for a particular instrument. Short-focus telescopes, as reflectors usually are, will not perform well with eyepieces which are designed for long-focus instruments, that is, refractors. Before turning to eyepieces in detail, there are one or two misconceptions which should be removed without delay.

Many people have no notion of the magnifying powers which can and should be used, and are under the impression that very high powers are not only the best but are the only ones which need be considered. No doubt it sounds impressive to talk about powers of several hundred diameters, but practical observers are not so impressed, as they never use higher powers than are necessary. High powers involve such disadvantages that they are used only when nothing lower will do. With a great magnification the image is faint, and every imperfection of the telescope is enhanced. Who wants a large, dim image which shows nothing more than detail visible with a smaller and far more convenient power?

For every telescope, there is a limit to the magnifying power on each end of the scale. The lower limit is determined by the pupil of the eye, and this varies, but perhaps ⅕ inch may be taken as the average diameter. It follows that if we use a power lower than 5 magnifications to the inch of aperture, the diameter of the pencil of rays emerging from the eyepiece will be larger than the pupil, so that not all the light gathered by the objective (or mirror) will be utilized. Virtually, we are cutting down the aperture. In the case of a 3-inch telescope we cannot use a power lower than 5×3, or 15; in the case of a 12-inch instrument, the limit is 60.

Theoretically, high powers have no limit, but it has been stated that 100 to the inch of aperture is as much as can ever be used to advantage. Even this is rarely if ever employed, and very seldom gives tolerable results. The power of a telescope to resolve detail is determined by its aperture. To see the two components of a binary star separated, or to glimpse two lunar peaks in their true guise, we must have a telescope of a certain aperture which is dependent upon the distance between the two stars or the two peaks. This distance is usually assumed to be between 4.56 and 5 seconds of arc per inch of aperture. In other words, a telescope with an object-glass 1 inch in diameter should just separate the two components of a binary star of separation between 4.65 and 5 seconds of arc. A 2-inch telescope should separate stars whose distance is half the former amount, that is, between 2.28 and 2.5 seconds, while a 10-inch telescope should resolve a pair whose separation is only 0.456 to 0.5 seconds of arc. In other words, the actual image formed by the objective will consist of two points of light just separated from each other, and this image is magnified by the eyepiece. How much magnification must we employ in order that the two points of light will be clearly seen as such?

This depends upon the ability of the eye to distinguish detail. Ordinary eyes can detect an object if its apparent diameter is not less than 1 minute of arc, but exceptionally keen eyes can detect features only ½ minute (30 seconds) of arc across. Such an eye would require a magnifying power of 6 in order to distinguish the components of a double star if the separation is 5 seconds of arc, if the telescope used has an aperture of 1 inch. It follows that a normal eye requires 3 times this amount, or 12 to the inch, to utilize the full resolving power of the instrument.

The magnifying power of any telescope may be found by dividing the focal length of the objective, or mirror, by the focal length of the eyepiece. If the objective has a focal length of 40 inches and the eyepiece a focal length of 1 inch, the magnification will be 40; if the focal length of the eyepiece is ½ inch, the magnification will be 80, and so on. It follows that an eyepiece will give different powers on different telescopes, according to the focal lengths of the telescopes concerned.

The eyepiece may be a single lens; alternatively it may be made up of two or more lenses, in which case the lens furthest from the eye is called the "field lens" and that nearest to the eye the "eye lens."

The *Huyghenian* eyepiece is perhaps the most common type. It consists of two plano-convex lenses (flat one side and convex on the other), both flat surfaces being turned towards the eye. The field lens has a focus 3 times that of the eye lens, and the lenses are fixed at a distance from each other equal to half the sum of their focal lengths. The Gorman Huyghenian has a meniscus field lens (that is, the face is concave). These eyepieces are suitable for refractors, as their residual chromatic aberration tends to correct that of the objective, but they are not well suited for reflectors unless the mirror is of long focus.

The *Ramsden* eyepiece is not achromatic, and consists of two equal plano-convex lenses, the convex sides facing each other and separated by either their focal length or ⅔ the focal length of either lens. In a modified form of the eyepiece, the eye lens is an achromatic combination. Most finder eyepieces are of the Ramsden type.

The *Kellner* eyepiece has a convex field lens, the radii of the surfaces being in the ratio of 2 to 3 with the deeper curve towards the eye. The eye lens is plano-convex, and separated from the field lens by its own focal length.

The *Tolles* negative eyepiece is in effect a Huyghenian made from a single glass cylinder with curved ends, the foci falling within the glass.

The *orthoscopic* is a positive eyepiece—so that unlike the Huyghenian, it can be used as an ordinary magnifying glass. It has a triple field lens, and a single eye lens.

The *monocentric* eyepiece consists of three lenses in contact cemented together, and has a rather small field of view.

The *Barlow* is an achromatic negative concave lens, which can be used in conjunction with any eyepiece to increase the power. It is placed within the focus of the objective, and forms an enlarged image further away than the primary image. The focal length (negative) is usually between 3 and 4 inches.

The *terrestrial* or erecting eyepiece consists of 4 lenses, virtually two Huyghenian eyepieces. That furthest from the eye often consists of a plano-convex field lens and a meniscus eye lens, while the combination nearest the eye may have a plano-convex field lens and a double-convex eye lens. The first combination produces an inverted image, and the second inverts this again, so that the final image is erect. It is possible to use an inverting prism and an ordinary eyepiece in place of the older type.

If the diameter of the field lens of a celestial eyepiece is made proportional to the focal length of the combination, the field of view is inversely proportional to the power.

Old-fashioned microscope eyepieces make fine low-power eyepieces for a telescope, but since their field lenses are sometimes 1½ or 1¾ inches in diameter it is generally necessary to fit a special draw-tube. They are also useful as comet eyepieces, and for viewing objects which require low powers and large fields of view.

The *equivalent focus* of any two-lens eyepiece can be found from the formula

$$\frac{f_1 \times f_2}{f_1 + f_2 - d},$$

where f_1 and f_2 are the focal lengths of the two lenses and d is their distance apart. To measure the focal lengths of eyepiece lenses, measure between the posterior focal centre of the field lens and the anterior focal centre of the eye lens. The anterior focal centre of a plano-convex lens coincides with the optical centre on the vertex of the curve, and the posterior focal centre is within the body of the lens at a distance from the vertex equal to ⅓ the thickness of the lens. The equivalent focal length of a Huyghenian eyepiece is approximately equal to ½ the focus of the field lens.

If the field lens of such an eyepiece is removed, the magnifying power is increased by ⅓, but definition is only sharp near the centre of the field of view.

An astronomical telescope should have at least three available eyepieces—one to act as a low power, not magnifying more than 8 times the diameter in inches of the objective or mirror; the second to act as a medium power, 20 to 30 times the diameter; and the third for use as a high power, 50 to 60 times the diameter. Hence for a 6-inch reflector, suitable eyepieces would have magnifying powers of (a) 48, (b) 120 to 180, and (c) 300 to 360. Large telescopes do not need, and in any case will not bear, eyepieces of such high ratios.

It is better to buy eyepieces than to attempt to make them. If they must be made, a good lathe is a necessity. According to the type of eyepiece desired, the lenses should be bought, care being taken with regard to the focal lengths. A piece of brass tubing is gripped in the self-centring chuck, and one end faced, bored out for about ¼ inch, and chased 50 threads to the inch. The field lens should just enter and rest on the bottom of the turned part. A collar is now turned from slightly larger brass tubing of sufficient thickness. Leave a narrow flange, and knurl-thread the body to fit the internal thread, boring out the centre. This should just touch the lens when the lens is screwed in. Another method is to bore the collar a little smaller than the lens, leaving a sharp edge of metal like a thin walled cylinder. When the lens is inserted, it is then spun in by pressing the edge over. The eye lens is smaller, and thus is usually mounted in this way. Shorten the tube, if necessary, until the lenses are at the correct distance apart. A stop may be turned, and pressed into the tube at the focus of the eye lens. Blacken the inside of the tube. Every care should be taken to ensure that the lenses are mounted square with the tube.

An eyepiece which has the field lens at the focus of the eye lens is an abomination, for every speck of dust on the field lens will be painfully evident!

The *solar eyepiece* is a device to permit safe observation of the Sun. It takes the form of two short tubes at right angles to each other. One fits the eyepiece draw-tube, while the other receives the actual eyepiece. A 10°-angle prism is inserted in the tube, which allows most of the Sun's light and heat to pass through, the remainder being reflected to form the image. It is necessary to use a prism and not a piece of glass with parallel sides—otherwise, a double image will result. The *star eyepiece* is similar, except that a totally reflecting prism is used, as the aim is now to transmit as much light as possible. Both these forms are known generally as *diagonals.*

Owing to the fact that the secondary mirror in a compound reflector (Gregorian or Cassegrain) greatly enlarges the primary image, the eyepieces needed are of much longer focal length than those suitable for use with the ordinary reflector or the Newtonian reflector. The two lenses forming the eyepiece of an oldtime Gregorian reflector have focal ratios of something like 2.5 to 1, the field lens being large and the mount massive.

The advantage of a Barlow lens is that one eyepiece, about ¾ focus, can be made to give a wide range of powers by varying the position of the Barlow and the eyepiece itself. It thus does away with a battery of eyepieces, and is easier in operation. While in America, Wilkins was given a *Goodwin Barlow,* complete with eyepiece, and this has been found to give excellent results on his short-focus 15¼-inch reflector. Another good eyepiece of similar type is that constructed and developed by the eminent British optician and amateur astronomer, H. E. Dall.

A Barlow lens is also of great use in astronomical photography, because it can be employed to project an enlarged image on to the plate. (See Chapter XI.)

An eyepiece should be an easy sliding fit into the drawtube, and should not be screwed in. Most small refractors have screwed-in eyepieces, the thread being what is humorously termed the "standard" astronomical thread. Actually, eyepieces supplied with a particular instrument will indeed screw in as planned, but it's long odds against their screwing in to any make of telescope. If we wish to use an eyepiece upon a telescope with which it was not originally supplied, it is advisable to carry a couple of strips of thin cardboard so as to pack up the "standard" thread of the first instrument to fit the second. Incidentally, this operation had better be done in daylight, as it is extremely difficult in the dark.

It is hardly necessary to point out that eyepieces are of varying quality. A bad eyepiece is one in which the lenses are of inferior glass, with scratched surfaces, placed at incorrect distances, out of centre, or set out of square. The field of view of a good eyepiece should give sharp definition right to the edge, without distortion of the image; and there should be uniform illumination. If you have a good eyepiece, take care of it. The less often it is dropped in the mud or onto hard ground, the better! Dirt on the lens will not improve matters. The procedure here is to prevent its getting on in the first place, but if a lens does become dirty the offending material must be removed by gentle sweeping. Vigorous rubbing will almost certainly result in the glass being scratched.

It sometimes happens that during an evening's observation with a hitherto satisfactory eyepiece, Mars will develop "wings" or a bright star an appreciably hazy surround. This will nearly always be due to dewing of the eye lens or (more rarely) the field lens. This must be removed either by gentle heating or by using a clean piece of cloth. Dewing often occurs in the autumn; it may also affect the objective of a refractor or one or both of the mirrors of a reflector. If the wings of Mars or the stellar hazes are always present, something is seriously wrong. If the telescope itself is above suspicion, the fault lies with the eyepiece, and this should be changed at once.

To find the angular dimensions of the field of view of an eyepiece, it is best to direct the telescope to a star close to the celestial equator, note the number of seconds it takes to cross the field of view, and then multiply by 15. This gives the value of the field in seconds of arc. If a star near the equator takes 120 seconds of time to cross the field of view, the field is half a degree in width, and will sometimes just show the whole of the Moon. The most suitable star for this purpose is probably Delta Orionis, the uppermost of the three stars in Orion's belt; others are Delta Ceti, Zeta Virginis and Alpha Aquarii.

Finally, it may be noted that if the eyepiece is required to focus on any arrangement of wires, as in a micrometer or a transit instrument, it must be a positive eyepiece. The ordinary Huyghenian is a negative eyepiece, and cannot be used for this purpose.

VII

USING THE TELESCOPE: THE MOON

IN NINE out of ten instances, the first object viewed by amateurs is the Moon. There are several reasons for this. The Moon is visible every month, and is so near to us that it not only shows a broad face or disk, but even to the naked eye reveals certain markings on its shining surface; it is easy to get into the field of view; and, most important of all, the most simple home-made telescope will reveal a great amount of detail. When it is added that the Moon is an almost completely airless globe, so that we can see its surface undimmed by cloud or mist, and that it is literally covered by the most interesting and fantastic detail, we need not wonder that the Moon is the favourite object for study.

The Moon is a small world, much smaller than the Earth, for it is only 2,160 miles in diameter. However, its small size is more than compensated for by its nearness, its distance being less than a quarter of a million miles. The Moon is the nearest to us of all celestial bodies, and with the finest instruments we can see objects on its surface which are only a couple of hundred yards in width. Moreover, the appearance is constantly changing as the sunlight sweeps over the surface. The deep black shadows to be seen when the sun is rising or setting on any part of the Moon have all gone by mid-day there; hence it is near lunar sunrise or sunset that the best views are obtained.

With the unaided eye, the Moon presents a curiously patchy or mottled appearance. In a telescope, these dark patches are seen to be great plains, while the brighter parts are plastered over with thousands of queer ring-like objects, the celebrated lunar craters. The craters are more or less circular areas, usually deeply sunken below the outer level, and surrounded by circular mountain ranges—sometimes perfect and complete, sometimes broken and discontinuous. Not only are the craters numerous, but they are also of enormous size. The largest of all, Bailly, is no less than 180 miles across. From this extreme we can find others of less and less diameter, right down to tiny pits a couple of hundred yards across. In addition to the craters, there are mountains, mountain ranges, hills and ridges, while in some places the surface is cracked, great yawning chasms opening out to our view. At sunrise, and again at sunset, every hill casts a long shadow; the cracks or clefts become long lines of blackness, while the craters look like huge cauldrons filled with ink.

The time which elapses from the time when the first ray of sunlight strikes a mountain peak until the moment when the last ray fades out at sunset is a fortnight, for on the Moon the Sun shines for 14 terrestrial days, and then remains below the lunar horizon for the next 14 days. At all times except very near full moon, when the Sun is shining directly upon the surface as we see it, and again at new moon when the unlit hemisphere is turned towards us, the shadow effects are very striking. Of course we do not see the mountains in profile, as we do those of the Earth; we view them as though from an aeroplane or rocket craft at a great height above the lunar surface. Only near the Moon's edge or "limb" can we see mountains in profile.

In order to explore the Moon and find one's way about amongst the confused jumble of craters and mountains, it is necessary to have a map. The beginner will want a clear and simple map, showing the principal mountains, plains, and craters. Naturally enough, the chief features have been named. Originally it was believed that the dark plains were seas; and although we now know that there is no moisture on the Moon, the plains retain their old names, such as Mare Imbrium (the Sea of Showers), Mare Nubium (the Sea of Clouds) and Sinus Iridum (the Bay of Rainbows). Craters are named after famous men; for instance one is named after Plato, another after Aristotle, a third after Julius Caesar. Those who require a simple map of the Moon will find their needs met by the small charts given in Moore's *Guide to the Moon* or Wilkins' *Our Moon*.

If we acquire a larger telescope, something more comprehensive will be required, while those who wish to make a serious study of the Moon will need the most detailed map, which is that of Wilkins.* When it is stated that this map is 8 ft. 4 in. in diameter, and that even on this scale it looks crowded in parts, some idea may be gathered of the amount of detail it contains. However, it is too detailed for the beginner, who should make a start with a more simple map. With such a guide and a few of the superb photographs now easily obtainable, the amateur will be provided with

* A reduced scale copy of this map is contained in *The Moon,* by the present authors, published in 1955.

material for many a delightful evening's work; and with the experience and knowledge thus gained, he can graduate to the larger maps.

We are not concerned with the various theories which have been advanced to account for the great craters and other features so clearly revealed in our telescopes. Almost certainly they were caused by intense volcanic action in the past, though some still consider them to be the scars resulting from meteoric bombardment, and numerous other theories have been put forward. Whatever the origin of the features, we want to know the best way to observe them.

For the minute features, such as pits, delicate craterlets and minute hillocks, we must observe near sunrise or sunset on that part of the Moon, when the sun's rays are nearly horizontal—or, in other words, as seen from that part of the lunar surface the Sun would be near the horizon. At this time the shadows are longest, and every little irregularity is clearly displayed. If we measure the length of a shadow in miles or kilometres we can easily find the height of the elevation responsible, provided that we know the height of the Sun above the horizon as seen from there. This depends upon the feature's distance from the "terminator," that is, the line dividing the sunlight from the darkened part of the Moon. On the Moon, a degree of a great circle, such as the equator, measures 18.8 miles.

Plane trigonometry can be used for the determination of moderate heights, especially around the centre of the disk. The formula is: $H = \tan A \times L$, where H is the height of the elevation, A is the altitude of the Sun as seen from the elevation, and L is the length of the shadow. The chief difficulty is to determine the precise length of the shadow, especially when it is remembered that as the Moon is a sphere we view many objects under conditions of foreshortening. The closer to the limb, the shorter the shadows; and the measured lengths become a progressively smaller fraction of the true lengths, that is, the length which would be measured by anybody viewing them square on.

Hence in finding the lengths of the shadows, this effect must be allowed for. The apparent length of the shadow is either measured directly with a micrometer, or else obtained by scaling on a photograph. Once we know the heights of a few elevations, those of others in the same locality can be estimated by using the formula

$$H = H' \frac{A \times B}{C \times D}$$

where H is the height of the unknown elevation, H' is the known height of another elevation, A is the length of the shadow cast by the elevation whose height is known and B its distance from the terminator, C is the length of the shadow of the unknown peak and D its distance from the terminator. Of course, all measurements must be in the same units, whether miles, yards, feet or metres. If measured at the telescope, the length of the shadow will be in seconds of arc, which must be converted into some unit such as the mile; in the case of a photograph, the scale must be found. For amateur study, this may be done with sufficient accuracy by scaling some formation whose diameter is known, whence the value in inches or centimeters can be deduced.

Apart altogether from this aspect of lunar study, there remains a great deal of most interesting and valuable work well within the capacity of a small or moderate-sized telescope. Occultations of stars and planets are not infrequent as the Moon moves across the heavens. Everyone knows that when the Moon is a crescent, the dark part can be seen shining with a dull greyish light which is due to our own world reflecting sunlight on to the Moon. Should the crescent Moon happen to pass in front of and occult a star or planet, an additional interest is given to the phenomenon, because the dark lunar edge can be watched getting nearer and nearer the star until the latter suddenly disappears. Since a planet is not a starlike point of light, but exhibits a definite disk, its disappearance is not instantaneous, but occupies several seconds. From new to full moon, the disappearance or immersion of a star takes place at the dark limb of the Moon, while the reappearance or emersion takes place at the bright, sunlit limb. After full moon, the sequence is reversed.

When the planet Jupiter has been occulted by the bright limb, some observers have reported a dusky shading fringing the limb—an appearance which has been attributed either to a feeble lunar atmosphere, or to the effects of local heating. Possessors of 3- or 3½-inch refractors are well equipped for occultation work, and this dusky fringe should be looked for during each planetary occultation. A good watch set by radio time signals will enable the precise time of disappearance or reappearance to be noted. Occultations are of importance to the professional astronomer, because they afford information as to the exact position of the Moon's limb, and thus of the Moon itself, at a given instant. The difference between the observed and the predicted place is an indication of the error of our lunar tables; occultations thus enable these tables to be corrected.

Another pleasant and instructive recreation is to survey the earthlit dark part of the Moon with a low power on a small telescope. On a fine evening, with the crescent Moon hanging in the western sky, a power of 20 or 30 on a 3-inch glass will reveal a good amount of detail on the dark portion. The chief seas and some of the brightest and the darkest craters are sometimes very distinct; such formations are Aristarchus, Plato, and Grimaldi.

In thus viewing the dark part of the Moon, we are observing it during the lunar night, when the temperature there is very low. This is the time to watch out for flashes or glows. Such phenomena have been reported from time to time and are possibly caused by meteors striking the surface. At times, the dark limb seems fringed with light to the naked eye, and the telescope reveals a number of bright patches, while Aristarchus is occasionally very well defined. Those people who get up before sunrise can observe the dark part when the Moon is a rapidly decreasing crescent only visible a little before dawn.

If such craters as Atlas, Alphons, Eratosthenes, Plato, Schickard and Grimaldi are observed from night to night, a number of dark spots will be noted, which change their shapes during the course of the long lunar day. The nature of these dark areas is still not known, and hence a careful and continuous scrutiny is of great scientific value. The size and intensity of a spot should be related to the colongitude, that is, the position of the sunrise terminator, or the line stretching across the Moon, along which the Sun is rising. The position is measured from the line on the meridian which passes from one pole across the centre of the disk when the Moon is in the state of mean libration, and thence to the other pole. Roughly speaking, the colongitude is 0° at First Quarter, 90° at Full Moon, 180° at Last Quarter and 270° at New Moon. The colongitude for each day is given in such publications as the *Nautical Almanac.*

Eclipses of the Moon are interesting phenomena, and are not infrequent (a list of those occurring from 1953 to 1987 is given in Moore's *Guide to the Moon*). Since the Earth casts an extensive shadow behind it into space, it follows that when the Moon is full it must pass near this shadow, generally either above or below. Sometimes the Moon passes into the shadow either entirely, in which case the eclipse is total, or partially, when the eclipse is partial. The most remarkable thing about a total eclipse is the dull red colour which the Moon then exhibits. Theoretically, the Moon should become invisible, because the solar light should be entirely cut off by the Earth; but our atmosphere acts as a sort of gigantic lens, and bends the sunlight inwards, thus lighting up the Moon. In so doing, the atmosphere acts as a filter, absorbing the blue rays and allowing the red to pass through; this, of course, explains the remarkable reddish hue seen during totality. Although an eclipse can be followed with the naked eye, a small telescope will add greatly to the spectacle, because the edge of the shadow can be followed as it creeps over the surface hiding crater after crater. When totally eclipsed, much detail on the surface can be seen through the telescope—among it the systems of bright rays which radiate from Tycho and other craters. These rays are the most mysterious of all lunar features, and are most prominent near full moon.

Exploration of the Moon is a fascinating study. There is

always something new to see, for the light and shade are constantly varying, making our satellite the most spectacular of all celestial bodies and the sole world of which we have really detailed knowledge.

VIII

USING THE TELESCOPE: THE PLANETS

ALTHOUGH it is perhaps true to say that lunar observation is the most fascinating branch of astronomy from the amateur's point of view, a vast amount of pleasure can be derived from studies of those other near neighbours of ours, the planets. Moreover, such studies can be extremely valuable, and a 6-inch reflector will enable useful work to be done, particularly on Jupiter. It must, however, be admitted that planetary work is not easy and requires considerable training of the eye, but the beginner must not be discouraged if at first he sees little; as he becomes accus-

Planet	*Mean distance from Sun in millions of miles*	*Periodic time*	*Axial rotation (equatorial)*	*Synodic period*	*Orbital eccen.*	*Diam. miles (equatorial)*	*Mass (Earth = 1)*
Mercury	36	88 days	88 days	116 days	0.206	3,100	0.04
Venus	67	224 days	30 days	584 days	0.007	7,700	0.83
Earth	93	365¼ days	23h. 56m.	—	0.017	7,926	1.00
Mars	141	687 days	24h. 37m.	780 days	0.093	4,200	0.11
Jupiter	483	11¾ yrs.	9h. 53m.	399 days	0.048	88,700	318
Saturn	886	29½ yrs.	10h. 14m.	378 days	0.056	75,100	95
Uranus	1,783	84 yrs.	10h. 45m.	370 days	0.047	32,000	15
Neptune	2,793	164¾ yrs.	15h. 45m.	367 days	0.009	27,600	17
Pluto	3,666	248 yrs.	? ?	366 days	0.248	3,600	?

tomed to using a telescope, he will see more and more.

At this point it will be of use to the reader to have a summary of the known data relating to the planets. The figures are based upon the most recent measures, though some of the values for the diameters and masses of the outer planets (Uranus, Neptune, and Pluto) are still uncertain.

The "synodic period" of the planet is the mean interval between successive inferior conjunctions in the case of the two planets closest to the Sun (Mercury and Venus), or between successive oppositions of the remaining planets (Mars and those more distant from the Sun). It is important to grasp the few technical terms in common use, so that a brief explanation will not be out of place here.

"The planets revolve round the Sun in ellipses, the Sun occupying one focus of the ellipse, the other focus being empty." So runs the famous First Law of Kepler, announced in 1609, at about the time that Galileo was experimenting with the earliest astronomical telescopes. It is, however, important to note that the planets move in orbits which are very nearly circular (apart from Pluto, which should probably not be ranked as a major planet at all). From an observational point of view, the departure from exact circularity is important only in the case of Mars, whose distance from the Sun varies from 129 million miles at perihelion (the closest point to the Sun) to 153 million miles at aphelion (farthest point). Fig. 16 shows the orbits of the Earth and Mars at their correct relative distances. For all practical purposes, we can take the Earth's distance from the Sun as constant at 93 million miles.

When the Earth, the Sun, and Mars are in a straight line, with the Earth in the middle, Mars and the Sun naturally appear to be opposite in the sky. Mars is then said to be in opposition, and is excellently placed for observation. This state of affairs occurred on June 25, 1954, and the positions of the two planets on that date are shown (E1, M1). The Earth takes a year to revolve round the Sun, and on June 25, 1955, had arrived back at E1. But Mars

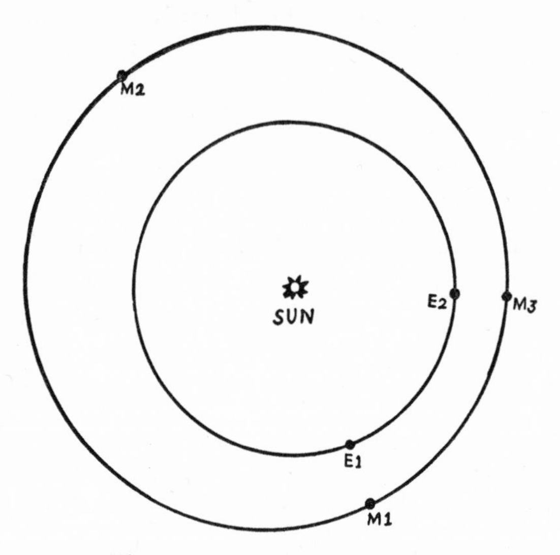

Fig. 16. Oppositions of Mars

was no longer at M1. It was moving more slowly in a larger orbit. It had only reached M2, on the far side of the Sun, and was unfavourably placed for observation. Before the three bodies were lined up once more, so that Mars was again at opposition, the Earth had to catch up to its slower-moving neighbor; it needed until September 11, 1956, to do so, when the Earth was at E2 and Mars at M3. There was thus no opposition of Mars in 1955. The interval between June 24, 1954, and September 11, 1956, is not far removed from the average synodic period of 780 days (in this case, it is actually a little longer).

A further point emerges from Fig. 16. On June 25, 1954, Mars was in opposition, but it was not at perihelion, so that it never came closer than 40,300,000 miles to the Earth. In 1956, however, opposition occurred with Mars almost exactly at perihelion, and the distance was reduced to 35,400,000 miles—less than at any time since 1924. By contrast, the opposition of 1948 occurred with Mars practically at aphelion, and the opposition distance was as much as 63,000,000 miles.

With Jupiter and the remaining outer giants, Saturn, Uranus and Neptune, the position is somewhat different (Pluto we can neglect, as it is of no interest to the amateur). The orbital eccentricities are less, and can be disregarded in the main, while the synodic periods are naturally shorter, so that each planet is well placed for several months in each year.

The two planets inside the Earth's orbit, Mercury and Venus, have their own way of behaving. For obvious reasons they can never come to opposition, and as they are always in much the same line of sight as the Sun they appear to follow the Sun round in the sky. The orbits of Venus and the Earth are shown in Fig. 17. With Venus at V1 and the Earth at E1, the Earth would, of course, be at opposition to an observer on Venus (supposing that one could exist there!). But to a terrestrial watcher, Venus is between Earth and Sun. It has no light of its own, and its night or non-lit hemisphere (blackened in the Figure) is turned towards us, so that the planet is "new" or invisible. As it moves on towards V2, a little of the daylit hemisphere begins to tilt towards us; at V2, the planet appears as a half ("dichotomy"), and increases gradually to "full" at V3, when, however, Venus is almost directly behind the Sun and is drowned in the solar glare. At V4, Venus is again a half, and returns to new at V1. The V1 position is known as Inferior Conjunction, while at V3 Venus is said to be at Superior Conjunction. Naturally, Mercury behaves in

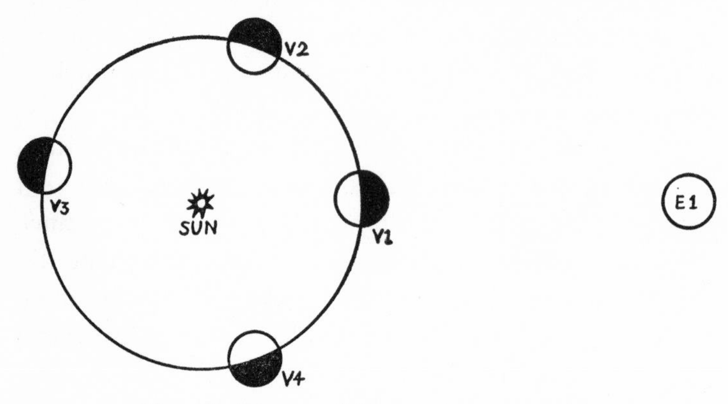

Fig. 17. Phases of Venus (not to scale)

the same way, though it is smaller, less reflective, and much closer to the Sun, so that it never becomes very conspicuous.

If an inferior planet is directly between Earth and Sun, it will, of course, appear as a black dot against the solar disk. Since the planetary orbits are slightly tilted, however, these transits of Mercury and Venus are decidedly infrequent.

With these brief notes upon the movements of the planets, we turn to physical observation. A few general remarks must first be made. A poor observation may be not only useless, but actually misleading, so that extreme care is necessary when a drawing is to be made; no detail should be recorded unless it has been seen with certainty, and written notes should also be made. Moreover, everything should be checked by comparing the completed drawing with the telescopic view. It is fatal to make a rough drawing at the telescope and then leave the "finished" copy until the following morning, as mistakes in interpretation are bound to occur. After a long sojourn in the outer cold of a winter night, it is tempting to act in this way; but the temptation must always be resisted!

Some observers make their "finished" drawings actually at the telescope. Others, less gifted artistically, make preliminary roughs, and then prepare a neater copy for their records. One method is as good as the other, provided that the final copy is thoroughly checked at the eyepiece.

A common error is that of trying to use too high a power. Further reference to this point is made in Chapter XIII, but it is as well to stress that a small, sharp image is far more useful than a larger but diffuse one. Venus is particularly troublesome in this respect, owing to the great brilliance of its disk.

It is absolutely vital to attach the following notes to each drawing: date (including year), time (G.M.T.), observer's name, type and aperture of telescope, magnifying power, and seeing conditions. If any of these points are omitted, the drawing at once loses most or all of its value.

Each planet has its own characteristics and its own special problems, and it is therefore necessary to consider each in turn.

MERCURY. The first serious telescopic observations of

Mercury were made towards the end of the eighteenth century, by Sir William Herschel, who could, however, detect almost no surface markings even with his great telescopes—the best of their time. His contemporary Johann Schröter, the pioneer lunar observer, did construct a chart of the planet, but this cannot be considered as reliable, and it was not until 1881–1889 that the first accurate chart was produced by the Italian observer Schiaparelli. During the present century, invaluable work has been done by the French observers, first by Antoniadi (with the Meudon 33-inch refractor) and subsequently by Lyot and Dollfus (with the Meudon 33-inch and the Pic du Midi 24-inch), while among British workers must be mentioned H. McEwen and M. B. B. Heath. A chart has also been drawn by the German astronomer, Dr. Werner Sandner. The chart shown in Fig. 18 shows the main surface details.

Mercury is a strange little world. Tidal interaction has resulted upon its rotation period becoming equal to its periodic time (88 terrestrial days), and it thus keeps the same face permanently sunwards, though as the orbit departs appreciably from the circular form there is a wide zone where the Sun appears to swing alternately above and below the horizon. To one side of this zone, the Sun is always above the Mercurian horizon, and at the hottest point the surface temperature must be over 700°F.; to the other side of the "twilight zone" it is perpetual night, and the temperature cannot be far above absolute zero. Mercury is, therefore, a planet of extremes.

Owing to its small mass. Mercury retains very little atmosphere. Definite indications of a gaseous mantle have, however, been detected by Dollfus; the ground density cannot exceed $^{3}/_{1000}$ of that of our own air, and a barometer would record a pressure of only about 1 millimetre. For all practical purposes, therefore, the Mercurian atmosphere

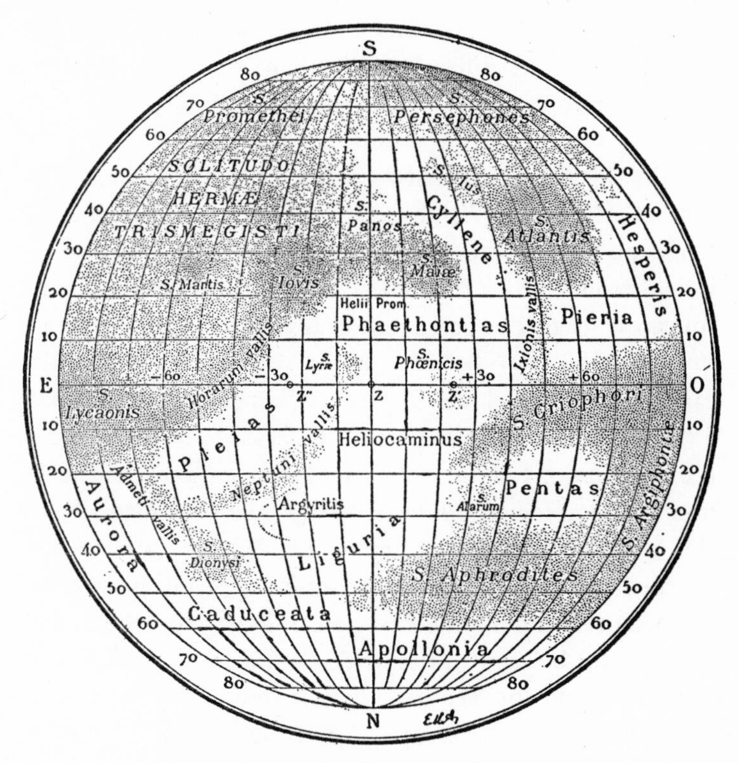

Fig. 18. Antoniadi's map of Mercury

can be disregarded. Both Schiaparelli and Antoniadi recorded frequent "clouds," hiding the surface features, but doubt upon the reality of these clouds has been cast by Dollfus, and the question remains open. If clouds do exist, they are naturally very different from those of the

Earth, and are probably mere dust-storms caused possibly by extensive vulcanism.

Schiaparelli and the French observers have done most of their best work with the Sun well above the horizon. With setting circles, Mercury can of course be found during the daytime without difficulty. With an altazimuth mount, the procedure is not easy, but with an ordinary equatorial Mercury can be found as follows: Using an almanac, ascertain the difference between the Sun's declination and that of Mercury. Withdraw the eyepiece, and point the telescope to the Sun (great care must be taken here, as it is dangerous to look directly at the solar disk, even when a suncap is used; the best method is to allow the Sun's rays to fall upon some reflecting surface, such as a piece of white cardboard). The Sun's apparent diameter is about half a degree. Take the number of degrees difference between the declinations of the Sun and Mercury, and double it; now raise or lower the telescope (as the case may be) by this number of Sun diameters. Leave the telescope untouched, and look through the finder or a low-power eyepiece shortly before the right ascension time, when Mercury should be seen in the field of view.

Study of the surface markings is difficult, and is quite hopeless with any telescope of less than about 10 inches, though the main dark areas, such as the Solitudo Criophori and the Solitudo Hermæ Trismegisti, can be glimpsed with smaller apertures.

If Mercury is a mountainous world, as is almost certainly the case, the terminator should appear rough, as in the case of the Moon; and in this way Schröter considered that he had detected a peak 11 miles high, though in the light of modern research this "discovery" must be regarded as highly dubious (to put it mildly). Terminator deformations can, however, be seen from time to time, and it is important to note them as accurately as possible. Do not, however, be deceived by the rippling of the terminator due to tremors in the terrestrial atmosphere; the serrated appearance sometimes drawn is due entirely to this cause.

With the naked eye, Mercury is never very conspicuous, but it can usually be seen several times a year. Sometimes, too, the planet may be found from its position relative to some more conspicuous object, such as Venus or the Moon. Transits across the Sun are rather rare; the last occurred in 1953, while the next will be on November 9, 1960. On these occasions Mercury appears telescopically as a small, sharp black dot.

It must be admitted that very little practical work on Mercury can be done by the owner of a small telescope, but it is always a source of satisfaction to pick up the elusive little "messenger of the gods" as it glitters shyly out of the morning or evening twilight.

VENUS. The first telescopic observations of surface features on Venus were made some 30 years after the invention of the telescope. Fontana drew some hazy shadings in 1643, and in 1727 Bianchini even drew up a chart of the surface details. Both Fontana and Bianchini believed that they were looking at a solid surface. They were, however, mistaken; Venus' actual surface is concealed by its dense, cloudy atmosphere. The exact nature of these clouds is uncertain, nor do we know much about the conditions in the lower atmosphere; in fact, although Venus is the nearest of the major planets, it is also the one about which we have learned the least.

Spectroscopic observations have shown that carbon dioxide is extremely abundant in the upper atmosphere of Venus; water vapour has not been detected. Until recently, it was generally thought that the whole planet was a howling desert, with a surface temperature higher than that of boiling water; but in 1954, theoretical investigations led two eminent American astronomers, Drs. Whipple and Menzel, to the conclusion that the surface is completely covered with water. The truth is that we simply do not know. We are even uncertain as to the length of the "day" on Venus; the best estimate is that the axial rotation period is about 30 times as long as ours.

Venus is a glorious object with the unaided eye, but its great reflecting power (59%) makes it difficult to study telescopically, and high magnification can seldom be used to advantage. It may be located during daylight in the same way as Mercury, but far more easily; it is indeed often bright enough to be seen with the unaided eye while the Sun is above the horizon. When near inferior conjunction, and thus a thin crescent, it has a larger diameter than when near superior conjunction, as it is nearer; but on the whole it is best to make drawings of a constant size—2 inches to the planet's diameter is a convenient scale.

The markings on the disk fall into three categories. There are diffuse dusky patches, small brightish areas, and areas which have been termed "polar caps," though these are certainly different in nature from those of the Earth or Mars and may not even mark the "geographical" poles.

The dusky patches may be seen with a 3-inch refractor, but are always hazy and ill-defined, so that they are difficult to draw accurately. The markings shift and alter in form from night to night, indicating that they are nothing more than high-altitude clouds, but sometimes the same feature can be followed for some time; on one occasion in 1954 Moore traced a dusky area for 10 days, though with modifications of shape. The bright patches also are diffuse, and purely atmospheric in nature.

The "polar caps" are often seen. Dr. J. C. Bartlett has expressed the opinion that they are true snowfields, though to the authors there seem insuperable objections to any such idea. Other authorities have dismissed them as mere contrast effects, but on the whole this is unlikely—though the dark bordering band often seen round them may be due partly to this cause—and they are well worthy of close study.

The terminator of Venus has been known to show marked projections and indentations, one of which led Schröter to assume the existence of a mountain 29 miles high! A lofty cloud, however, will catch the sunlight as efficiently as a lofty peak, and this seems a much more probable explanation. One of these terminator deformations is shown in Fig. 19.

The point at which Venus becomes a perfect half is known as "dichotomy." Since the orbit is known with high precision, it should be possible to predict the time of dichotomy to within a minute or so; nevertheless, the theoretical time of dichotomy is often badly wrong. In the winter of 1953, for instance, dichotomy should have occurred on February 3, whereas several observers recorded a straight terminator a week earlier. On the other hand, dichotomy in the autumn of 1951, when Venus was a morning star and therefore waxing, was over a week late. It should have occurred on November 14, but did not actually do so until November 26. These discrepancies were noticed by Schröter a century and a half ago, but have not so far been explained, though they are certainly due to

Patrick Moore

Fig. 19. Terminator deformation on Venus

some effect caused by the atmosphere of the planet. The amateur can do useful work by comparing the theoretical time of dichotomy with that actually observed.

Professor Percival Lowell, best remembered for his work on Mars, made drawings of Venus showing straight linear features described by him as being like steel engravings. Similar linear features have been drawn by other observers (Fig. 20), but are purely illusory.

It has often been stated that Venus is best seen in a small telescope, larger apertures causing distortion of the image owing to the unsteadiness of the Earth's atmosphere. This is not, however, the case. The authors have found that when Venus is observed first with a small telescope and then with a larger one, the true features—the hazy patches and bright areas—are seen more clearly with the greater aperture; it is significant that the false linear features appear only on drawings made with small, totally inadequate instruments.

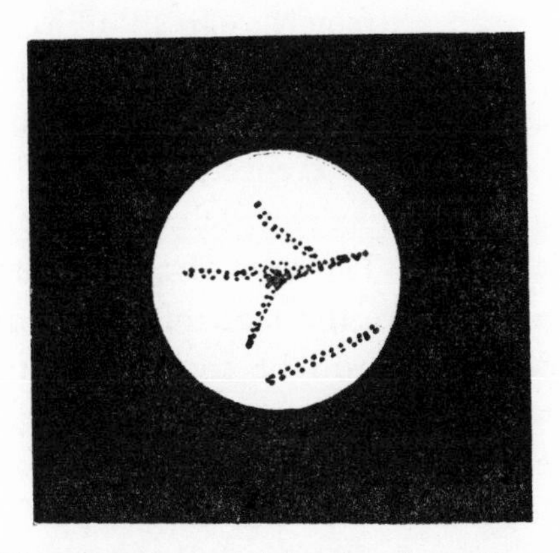

Fig. 20. Typical false detail on Venus

The appearance of the "earthshine" on the Moon is well known (see Chapter VII). Curiously enough, a similar appearance has often been seen on Venus; the unlit hemisphere at times appears clearly, glowing against the dark background. This appearance is known as the "Ashen Light," and was discovered by Schröter. Its existence cannot be doubted; it can be seen even with small telescopes, and is definitely not due to contrast. Venus has no moon, so that illumination by a nearby body cannot be responsible, and the cause of the Ashen Light is still unknown, though it may well be due to intense auroræ in the upper atmosphere of Venus.

Transits of Venus are most interesting; but they need hardly be discussed here, as the next will not take place until the year 2004!

MARS. It is probably true to say that of all the objects in the heavens, Mars holds the most fascination for the amateur observer. It is therefore doubly unfortunate that the Red Planet is an extremely difficult object to observe properly. Its movements have already been described, and we know that it comes to opposition at intervals of as much as 780 days or so; moreover, it is a small world, and only shows detail in a moderate telescope when fairly near the opposition point. The user of a 6-inch reflector will therefore have to make the most of his opportunities, as useful observing time will be confined to two or three months every alternate year.

Mars is the most Earthlike of all the planets. It is smaller, and has a thinner atmosphere, which appears to consist mainly of nitrogen and is deficient in both oxygen and water vapour. We can thus see the true surface, not a mere cloudy vista as with Venus, and the main features were recorded as long ago as the seventeenth century—a drawing made by Huygens in 1659 shows them clearly—while a good map was produced in 1840 by the German observers Beer and Mädler, better known for their work in connection with the Moon.

The most prominent features of the disk are the polar caps, first seen by Cassini in 1666. Any small instrument will show them when Mars is favourably placed, and there is no longer any doubt that they are made up of some icy or snowy deposit, so that they are basically similar to the polar caps of the Earth. They are, however, very thin.

The tilt of Mars' axis is much the same as ours, so that the seasons are analogous, though longer; when spring comes to a Martian hemisphere, the polar cap melts very rapidly, showing that it cannot be of depth greater than a few inches. At its greatest extent, a polar cap may extend half-way to the equator, though at minimum it is reduced to a tiny speck—the southern cap has even been known to disappear completely for a time.

The caps do not melt regularly, but show irregular outlines, with detached portions. From this, Dollfus has inferred the existence of plateaux several thousands of feet high in the polar zones, though in general Mars is not a mountainous planet. Moreover, the melting cap shows a dark border or "band" round its edge. This band is unquestionably real; possibly it is due to the moistening of the ground by material released by the melting cap, so that the ground shows up as darker until the marshiness dries up.

The dark areas of Mars can also be seen with a small instrument. Up to some sixty years ago, they were believed to be seas, but it is now certain that there are no large sheets of water on Mars, so that the dark regions are more probably made up of tracts of low-type vegetation. This theory is supported by the fact that as the polar cap melts, releasing moisture, the adjacent dark areas darken and harden as though coming to life, and a wave of darkening spreads equatorwards. Superimposed on this seasonal cycle are local variations; sometimes a dark area will spread on to a nearby bright region, remaining extended for some years before returning to its original form, and some areas, such as the Solis Lacus (Lake of the Sun) show abrupt, irregular alterations in form and intensity.

The reddish-ochre areas, which cover most of the Martian surface and give the planet its well-known ruddy hue, may best be described as deserts—not of sand, but of dust. The surface coating may well be made up of brownish, fine-grained felsite.

Mars' rotation period is 24 hours 37 minutes, not unlike our own, so that it is never possible to see every feature on the map during the course of a single night's observation. The longitude of the central meridian can be worked out from the simple tables given in the *Observer's Handbook.* The difference between our rotation period and that of Mars is about half an hour, so that a feature on the central meridian at any particular moment will again be on the central meridian half an hour later on the following night. The feature concerned can thus be observed at some period or other for several consecutive nights, until it is finally carried beyond the limb; the original conditions will recur after a lapse of about 40 days.

A 6-inch reflector is just about adequate for proper work on Mars, but only for a short period at each opposition, and for really valuable observations a larger telescope is needed. With a 10- to 12-inch reflector, magnifying powers of from 300 to 400 are recommended.

When starting to make an observation of Mars, it is important to look up the extent of the slight but significant phase, using an almanac, and to prepare a disk accordingly. (This can, of course, be neglected near opposition, when the planet appears virtually circular.) When the planet is in the field of view, scrutinize it for some time to survey the main details—preferably without working out the longitude of the central meridian beforehand, in order to avoid any possible prejudice. Then draw in the main details, and affix the time to the sketch. Do not subsequently alter these main outlines with regard to their position in relation to the central meridian, as Mars is rotating all the time, causing perceptible drift of the markings across the disk from east to west. The finer details can be added at more leisure, and written notes made, while the final drawing should always be checked and a higher power tried to see whether it will give any better results. As with Venus, a set scale of 2 inches to the planet's diameter is most convenient.

Thin though it is, the Martian atmosphere contains clouds. These are of two fundamental types—high-level objects made up probably of ice crystals, and lower-level "yellow clouds," which seem to be dust storms. Some of the latter are of vast extent; in 1911, for instance, Antoniadi, at Meudon, recorded an immense veil which hung over the southern hemisphere, concealing many of the well-known dark areas and persisting for weeks. Shorter-lived clouds are much more frequent. In May 1952, for instance, the authors, using Wilkins' 15¼-inch reflector at Bexleyheath, drew a very prominent cloud over the bright ochre tract known as Æria. This was also seen on the following night by Moore with his 12½-inch, and was reported by other observers using instruments of 8- and 6-inch aperture. Clouds are also seen near the terminator when Mars shows an appreciable phase, causing deformations, and now and then something much more unusual is seen; on December 8, 1951, for instance, the eminent Japanese observer Saheki observed a curious, short-lived bright spot over the Tithonius Lacus, attributed by some to a volcanic explosion, but much more probably due to some cloud phenomenon.

The famous "canals" of Mars are often drawn with clarity and precision by observers using telescopes of from 3 to 6 inches in aperture. In point of fact, it is absolutely impossible to see a canal with any such instrument, so that not the slightest reliance can be placed upon the drawings concerned—many of which have found their way into print! That the canals exist is undoubted; Dollfus, at the Pic, has stated that under conditions of excellent seeing they are broken down into "fine structure" of spots and streaks. On the other hand, it is most improbable that they are anything but natural features, and Lowell's idea of them as being vast artificially constructed waterways has been discredited. As they take part in the general seasonal cycle of the polar caps, it is logical to assume that they are made up of vegetation, though why vegetation should be arranged in linear streaks remains one of the greatest mysteries of modern astronomy.

Mars has two satellites, Phobos and Deimos. Both are minute (their diameters are perhaps 12 and 6 miles respectively), and are therefore hard to see, even when Mars is close. Wilkins has seen both with his 15¼-inch, and Moore has glimpsed Phobos with his 12½-inch, but not easily; and in 1954 Wilkins found that even the great Yerkes 40-inch refractor would not show Deimos as anything but an excessively minute disk.

THE MINOR PLANETS. Revolving round the Sun between the orbits of Mars and Jupiter are numerous small worlds, known as Minor Planets or Asteroids. Most of them are extremely minute. The largest (Ceres) is some 500 miles across, while only one other (Pallas) exceeds 300 miles.

The brightest of them, Vesta (diameter 240 miles), can just be seen with the unaided eye under favourable conditions; the rest require instrumental aid. Dr. R. S. Richardson has estimated the total number of minor planets as 44,000.

Needless to say, no surface details can be made out on these tiny worlds. It is, however, interesting to hunt for asteroids, and to check their positions and brilliancies; as some of the computed orbits are uncertain, amateurs can do valuable work in this direction. One of the leading British observers of minor planets, Lieutenant-Colonel G. E. B. Stephenson, uses a 6-inch reflector made by himself.

In order to identify an asteroid, first look up the predicted position among the stars, using an almanac. The star-field is then examined at the telescope. Very often the minor planet will not be found at the first attempt, as it looks exactly like a star, and the whole field will have to be drawn, using some known star as a flagpost. If the same field is again drawn on the following night, the true stars will be seen in the same relative positions, but the minor planet will have moved, thus betraying its identity. Fig. 21 shows the shift in the minor planet Astræa over a period of two days, as observed by Mrs. G. E. Stone in 1954 with a 2½-inch refractor.

One or two minor planets have interesting orbits. Eros, an irregularly-shaped body with a longer diameter of about 15 miles, swings in within the orbit of Mars, and can pass within 14 million miles of the Earth; smaller objects come even closer, the record being held by a worldlet named Hermes, which brushed past us in 1937 at a distance of only 400,000 miles. The minor planet Icarus has an orbit which carries it to within 18 million miles of the Sun (closer than Mercury), while Hidalgo has its aphelion at the mean distance of far-away Saturn, and the "Trojan" asteroids move almost in the orbit of mighty Jupiter. These objects are, however, too faint to be of any practical interest to the amateur observer.

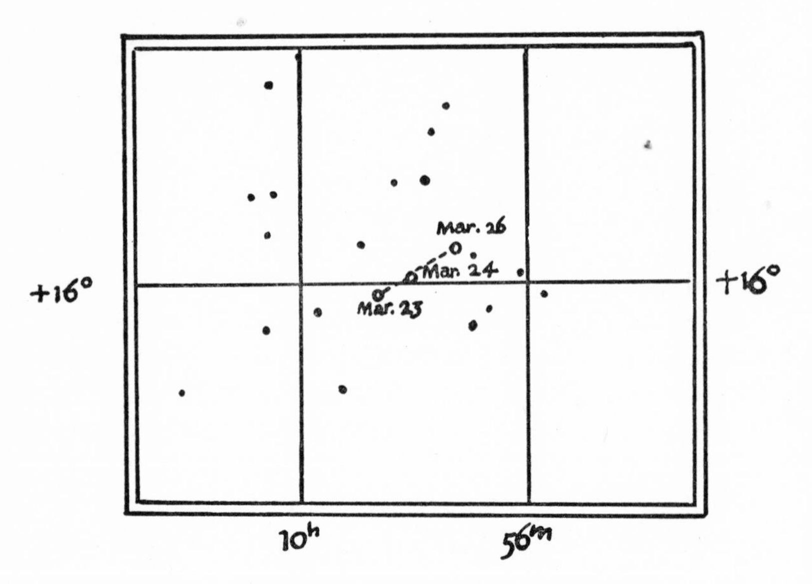

Fig. 21. Movement of the Minor Planet Astræa
1. 1954 March 23, 22^h 30^m
2. " " 24, 22^h 15^m
3. " " 26, 23^h
Magnitude 8.9. Opposition 1954 February 22 (mag. 8.7)
Observations by Mrs. G. E. Stone, 2½-in. O.G.

JUPITER. Much of our knowledge about the physical characteristics of Jupiter is due to amateur observers—in particular to the members of the B.A.A. Jupiter Section, directed for many years by the Rev. T. E. R. Phillips. Jupiter is in fact the ideal object of study for our amateur equipped with a moderate telescope of from 5 to 8 inches in aperture.

Jupiter is totally unlike the Earth. Up to recent years, it was believed to possess a central core of rock, overlaid by a layer of ice which was in turn overlaid by a deep gaseous "atmosphere" made up principally of hydrogen, helium, and two most unpleasant compounds, ammonia and methane. It is now thought that the constitution of the planet is rather different from this, but at any rate there can be no doubt about the nature of the outer gases, nor can it be doubted that the visible features—the belts and spots—are purely "atmospheric." Moreover, the planet does not rotate as a rigid body would do. Parts of the surface rotate at different rates; and the Jovian markings shift and change, so that there is always something new to see on the face of the Giant Planet.

Jupiter is markedly flattened at the poles, and this polar compression must never be neglected when a drawing is to be made. If trouble is experienced in preparing suitably flattened disks, it is a good idea to make one fair copy, and to have numbers of disks printed from it. Alternatively, stencilling may be used.

The most prominent features of the Jovian disk are the cloud belts. These were seen very soon after the original invention of the telescope, and any tiny instrument will show some of them. Spots, notches, festoons, and other complex features appear when a larger aperture is used, and a 6-inch will reveal a tremendous amount of detail when the disk is active.

In drawing Jupiter, first prepare a disk in which the polar compression has been allowed for, and then go to the telescope and sketch in the main details (the chief belts, disturbed areas, and spots). This basic sketch should be completed as quickly as possible, owing to the rapid rotation of the planet on its axis, and the exact time noted. Then start work upon the finer details, changing to a higher power if necessary, paying particular attention to details

Fig. 22. Nomenclature of Jupiter

such as relative intensities and irregularities in the outlines of the belts. Finally, make appropriate written notes, and check the entire drawing against the telescopic view. The time of the drawing should be taken as the moment when the basic outline is completed, and should be given to the nearest half-minute.

The chief markings on the disk are named as shown in the diagram (Fig. 22). Needless to say, this diagram is only an average representation. There are times when the south equatorial belt (S.E.B.) is as prominent as its northern counterpart; on other occasions, as in the autumn of 1951, the S.E.B. may be obscure, the S.T.B. (south temperate belt) being prominent. A belt may be double, or perhaps absent; extra belts may be detected; bright and dusky zones may appear—there is no end to the infinite variation of the Jovian disk. If a belt is double, the two components are indicated by the suffix n (north) or s (south); $N.E.B._{n}$, $N.E.B._{s}$ and so on. Common abbreviations in nomenclature are: P = polar, T = temperate, E = equatorial, pr = preceding (western), f = following (eastern), Z = zone, B = belt, D = disturbance.

The equatorial region, bounded by the north edge of the S.E.B. and the south edge of the N.E.B., has an average rotation period of 9 hours 50 minutes, and is known as System I. The rest of the surface (System II) has an average rotation rate about 5 minutes longer, though various special features have their own independent ways of behaving. It is important to differentiate between these two distinct rotational systems when we come to consider the taking of transits.

To take a transit, all that need be done is to estimate the moment at which a particular feature crosses the central meridian of Jupiter. Accurate timing is necessary, to the nearest minute or half-minute, and after a little practice the observer will find himself able to make estimations to a high degree of accuracy. The importance of these transit observations is that the longitude of the feature concerned can be worked out from tables, and hence an accurate rotation period for it derived.

Tables for the longitude of the central meridian at any

moment are given in the *Observer's Handbook,* hence as soon as the transit time of any particular feature has been measured, its longitude can be calculated by simple addition. Care must be taken to use the tables relevant for the particular rotational zone (I or II) in which the feature lies. A typical series of transits, taken by Moore in 1951, is given here.

1951 September 17. 8½-inch reflector, × 350. Conditions good, with steady seeing. Considerable structure in the three main belts, with a disturbed equatorial zone. No colour noted.

Time G.M.A.T.	*Feature*	*Longitude System I*	*Longitude System II*
10.59	Hump, N.E.B.	175.0	—
11.04	Centre of Break, $N.T.B._n$	—	88.9
11.07	Pr. part of condensation f. break, $N.T.B._n$		90.7
11.10	Centre of v. slight broadening, S.E.B.	181.7	92.5
11.14	Centre of spot. $N.E.B._n$	184.1	—
11.19	Pr. part of condensation, N.N.T.B.	—	97.9
11.26	F. hump, N.E.B.	191.4	—
11.29	Very slight hollow, $S.T.B._s$	—	103.9
11.40	Centre of white spot, $N.E.B._s$	199.9	—
11.59	F. end of slight broadening, N.N.T.B.	—	122.0
12.00	F. end of broad section, $N.T.B._n$	—	122.6
12.02	F. hump of spot, $N.E.B._s$	213.3	—

(Both Systems are given for the transit of 11.10, as the feature lay in a position such that it might be considered as belonging to either zone.)

It will also be useful to give the exact method of working, using the tables for the longitude of the central meridian and the amount of longitude change in intervals of mean time. Let us consider the transit of 10.59, which is, of course, System I.

In the tables, it is found that on September 17, at 6 hours

G.M.A.T., the longitude of the central meridian was 352.7. The change in 4 hours is 146.3; this gives a total of 499.0. Subtract 360; this gives 139.0. The amount of change in 50 minutes is 30.5, and in 9 minutes 5.5; adding these (to make 59 minutes) the final result is 175.0, which was the longitude of the hump on the N.E.B. observed to transit at that moment.

The only apparently semi-permanent feature on Jupiter is the "Great Red Spot," which became conspicuous in 1878 but which can be traced upon much earlier sketches. Its exact nature is unknown, but it is probably some sort of solid body floating in the Jovian clouds. Its former reddish hue has now faded, and in fact the vivid disk colours described by earlier observers are no longer marked, indicating some long-period variation in the atmosphere of Jupiter. Most of the spots and minor features are short-lived, lasting for a few months at most; now and then objects of unusual interest are seen, such as the strange spots moving in a "circulating current" in the S.T.Z. recorded between 1930 and 1934. There are also occasional violent upheavals in the region of the S.E.B., one of which occurred as recently as 1949.

Of the twelve satellites of Jupiter, only four (Io, Europa, Ganymede and Callisto) are within the range of normal telescopes. They were discovered by Galileo in 1609, and their eclipses, occultations, and transits across the face of Jupiter are fascinating to watch, even with a small instrument such as a 3-inch refractor. It is also of interest to compare the relative brilliances of the four; Callisto, in particular, shows peculiar and so far unexplained variations. With giant telescopes, surface features can be seen, as is demonstrated by the fine drawings made by the French observers at Meudon and the Pic. These surface markings are, however, quite beyond the range of most instruments, and the detailed drawings produced by observers working with apertures of 6, 10, or even 15 inches can be largely disregarded.

SATURN. There can be no doubt that Saturn is by far the loveliest object in the entire heavens. This is not because of its globe, which is basically similar to that of Jupiter, though with less prominent belts and few spots, but because of its unique system of rings. These rings were first seen by Galileo, but not clearly enough for him to determine their true nature, and it was left to Huygens, some forty-five years later, to show that Saturn was surrounded by a flat ring system "inclined to the ecliptic, and nowhere touching the body of the planet." Although the rings appear as a solid sheet, they are not actually so; they are composed of countless tiny pieces of matter, each of which revolves round Saturn in the manner of a satellite.

Saturn is a much more quiescent world than Jupiter. Here again we have the difference in rotation periods for different zones; the equatorial period is 10 hours 14 minutes, but near the poles this increases to something like 10 hours 30 minutes. Exact information is rather difficult to obtain, as well-marked features are rare. Occasionally a spot makes its appearance (the best-known of recent years being that of 1933, which was most conspicuous, and easily seen by Moore with a 3-inch refractor), but is usually short-lived. Needless to say, there is always the chance of making a spectacular discovery; the 1933 spot was found by an amateur, W. T. Hay, using a home-made reflector.

When features such as this are seen, the procedure for observation is much the same as in the case of Jupiter; but in general, interest will be focused on the rings, which are of immense breadth (170,000 miles) but remarkably thin (less than 50 miles, possibly less than 10). A diagram of the system is given in Fig. 23. It will be seen that there are three main rings:

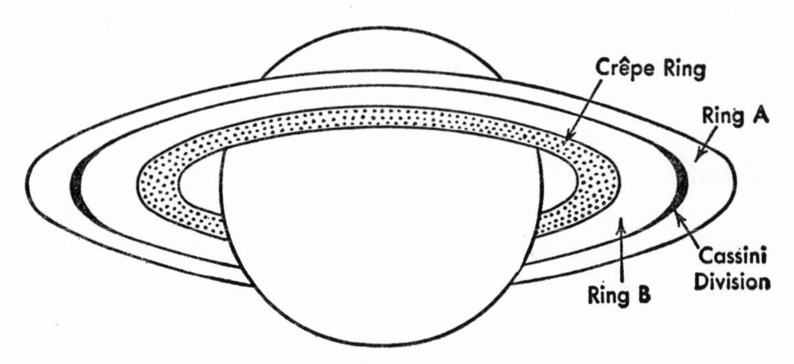

Fig. 23. Saturn and its rings

Ring A, 10,000 miles wide, and fairly bright;

Ring B, 16,000 miles wide, and very bright;

Ring C (the Crêpe or Dusky Ring), 10,000 miles wide, and semi-transparent.

Rings A and B are separated by a division known as Cassini's Division, after its discoverer, 1,700 miles wide. This and the other Divisions are due to the gravitational pulls of Saturn's nine satellites, particularly the closest to the planet, Mimas. The Cassini gap can be seen with a 3-inch refractor when the ring system is well displayed.

In Ring A itself is another division, Encke's, much less obvious than that of Cassini. Other divisions have been reported (two in Ring B, one in the Crêpe Ring, and one separating Ring B from the Crêpe Ring), but these are delicate objects, and require large apertures.

There is a further suspected ring, lying outside A and thus the most distant of the rings from the planet. It has been reported at various times since 1907, and has been seen in recent years by several observers, including R. M. Baum in England and T. L. Cragg in America. Moore failed to find it in 1953 with the Meudon refractor, and Wilkins was similarly unsuccessful in 1954 at Yerkes, but nevertheless it probably does exist; it is significant that although the Crêpe Ring is not now considered at all a difficult object for a moderate telescope (it is very evident with a 6-inch when well placed), it escaped detection altogether until 1850, when it was discovered independently by Lassel and Bond.

The rings cast shadows on the disk, and similarly the disk casts shadow on the rings. These shadows should be drawn with the utmost care. The relative brilliancies of the rings should also be noted—variations have been suspected, though their cause would be hard to explain—and divisions searched for. Apart from Cassini's, these divisions will generally be seen only at the ansæ or "ends" of the rings. Colours should also be noted. The Crêpe Ring, in particular, has been thought to fluctuate slightly in hue; Wilkins in 1954 noted it as being distinctly brownish.

The thinness of the rings means that the apparent aspect of the system alters very considerably. When turned edge-on to the Earth, as happens every 14 years, it appears as a thin line, and for a few days the rings disappear altogether in a small telescope. This last occurred in 1951. At intermediate times, the rings are "open"; maximum opening will next occur in 1958. Needless to say, observations of the divisions and similar phenomena can be made only when the system is fairly open, but at the times of edge-on presentation equally interesting observations can be carried out. Strange "humps" along the hair-line of light have been recorded, and sometimes the ansæ are unequal in brilliancy. As we have no idea of the cause of these irregularities, it is most important to study them with the utmost care.

Saturn is not an easy object to draw, but in general there is no "short cut"; one outline of the ring system may be used for several consecutive nights, but owing to the changing angle of presentation it will be necessary to make a new outline at least every week. Nor should the polar compression be neglected. Saturn is in fact the most flattened of all the planets, and the difference between its polar and equatorial diameters amounts to over 6,000 miles.

Colour and intensity observations of the disk and of the ring system should be made whenever possible, using an intensity scale of from 10 (black shadow) to 0 (brilliant white). Average intensities are: equatorial zone, 3; ring B, 3; ring A, 5 to 6; ring C, 7; main belts, 6 to 8; Cassini Division, 8 to 8½.

Occasionally, Saturn will occult a star. The star will then be seen passing behind the ring system, and should be closely watched, every fluctuation being noted; these rare occultations are in fact of the utmost importance, since they enable estimations to be made of the transparency of the various rings and divisions.

Saturn has 9 satellites, named, in order of increasing distance from the planet: Mimas, Enceladus, Tethys, Dione, Rhea, Titan, Hyperion, Iapetus and Phœbe. Titan can be seen with any 2½-inch to 3-inch telescope (it is, in fact, of greater diameter than Mercury, and is the largest satellite in the Solar System), while a 3-inch will also show Iapetus, Rhea, Dione and Tethys. A 6-inch will reveal all these, plus Enceladus; an 8-inch reflector will also catch Mimas, and Hyperion when favourably placed. Phœbe is much more difficult. The most interesting of these nine moons is Iapetus, which is variable in light. It is far brighter when west of Saturn than when east of the planet; if (as is highly probable) it obeys the general satellite law of keeping the same face turned permanently towards its primary, it must have a rough surface of unequal reflecting power. A tenth satellite, announced by Pickering in 1904 and named Themis, has not been confirmed, and probably does not exist.

Surface detail on Titan has been seen at the great observatories, but this detail is of course far beyond the range of ordinary telescopes.

URANUS. This planet, discovered by Sir William Herschel in 1781, can just be seen with the unaided eye if its position is known. Owing to its remoteness, it is very difficult to study, but seems to be built upon the same general pattern as Jupiter and Saturn—though it is considerably smaller and less massive.

A strange feature concerning Uranus is the tilt of its axis, which is actually more than a right angle—98 degrees—so that unlike the other planets, Uranus rolls along in its orbit almost pole-first. As it takes 84 years to complete one revolution around the Sun, the seasons there must be most peculiar! There are times when the pole is pointed towards the Earth, and appears in the centre of the apparent disk; this was the case in 1945. At other times, the equator is presented.

In small telescopes, Uranus appears as a small greenish disk, easily distinguished from a star. To find it, first look up its position in the *Observer's Handbook* or an almanac, and then sweep for it with the finder or a low-power eyepiece. This may take some time on the first occasion when Uranus is sought, but once the star-field is known the planet may be found rapidly and without the slightest trouble. During 1954, Uranus was in the same finder field as the third-magnitude star Delta Geminorum.

Surface details are hard to make out, and once again the detailed drawings produced with the aid of small apertures must be discounted, but valuable work can be done with regard to the planet's apparent brilliancy. This can be estimated by comparing it with nearby stars of known magnitude. (For an explanation of magnitude, see Chapter IX.) The average value is 5.5, but there are strange fluctuations, some of which seem to be periodical and others not. Magnitude estimations are therefore of great value. The important observations carried out by A. P. Lenham in 1953 and 1954, which have led to a revision in the accepted value of the magnitude, were carried out entirely with a 6-inch reflector.

Uranus has five satellites, four of which (Ariel, Umbriel, Titania, and Oberon) are of some size, the fifth (Miranda) excessively faint. Titania is the brightest of the five, but even so is beyond the range of any telescope less than 10 inches in aperture.

NEPTUNE. Neptune was discovered in 1846, after calculations by two mathematicians, Le Verrier in France and Adams in England, had indicated its probable position. It is slightly smaller, slightly denser, and slightly more massive than Uranus, but all things considered, the two worlds may be considered as true twins.

Neptune is of the eighth magnitude and thus totally invisible with the naked eye, but may be found telescopically in the same manner as Uranus. At present (1955) it lies in the constellation Virgo, near the fifth-magnitude star 82 Virginis. It appears telescopically as a minute bluish disk; surface details are lacking, and the light does not seem to show the same fluctuations as that of Uranus, perhaps because the tilt of its axis is more normal (29 degrees). Magnitude estimations are, however, of value.

PLUTO, discovered by Tombaugh in 1930 on the basis of calculations by Lowell, is a peculiar body. It appears to be small—the most recent estimates of the diameter give a value of 3,600 miles—and has a strange orbit that at perihelion swings it closer to the Sun than is Neptune. As the periodic time is very long, perihelion will not next occur until the year 1989. Further details would be out of place in this book, as Pluto is of no interest to the amateur observer; observers with apertures of 12 inches or greater may, however, care to look for it. At present (1955) it lies in Leo, between the stars Epsilon and Xi Leonis. Even the 200-inch reflector on Mount Palomar will not show it as a perceptible disk.

From the above notes, it will be seen that there is a wide field of research open to the amateur in the field of planetary observation; indeed, it has often been said that the planets belong to the amateurs. There is a great deal in this remark. Professional astronomers spend most of their observing hours photographing the distant spiral nebulæ and the faint variable stars far beyond the reach of smaller instruments; but the average professional astronomer spends very little time in studying our nearest neighbours in space—those of our own system. In general, he prefers to leave them alone, and thus unwittingly gives the amateur with the home-made telescope his chance to contribute something really useful to the great science of astronomy.

IX

USING THE TELESCOPE: THE STARS

It is an undoubted fact that most books devoted to observational astronomy tend to concentrate upon solar, lunar, and planetary work. There is, of course, an excellent reason for this; the Solar system is the domain of the amateur, whereas professional astronomers, with their powerful and complicated instruments, spend most of their time in studying the stellar heavens. Both the present authors are lunar observers, and have to confess that they seldom look at a star except to test the telescope or to show a visitor something really spectacular! Yet there is a wide field of work open to the owner of a small instrument —particularly with regard to variable stars—and this branch of amateur astronomy should on no account be overlooked.

Stellar astronomy covers a vast field. Questions relating to the nature of a star, internal constitution, source of energy, and process of evolution are quite beyond the range of this book. However, it is necessary to give a brief résumé of some of the knowledge that has been accumulated during the past few hundred years.

As everyone knows, the Sun is a star—and far from being an exceptional one. Many of the stars we can see on any clear night are much more luminous. Rigel in Orion, for instance, shines with a brilliance equal to 18,000 Suns; Deneb in Cygnus would match at least 10,000, while the lovely southern star Canopus, unfortunately never visible from these latitudes, has a luminosity 80,000 times that of the Sun. Even Canopus is not the supreme searchlight of the heavens. S. Doradus, also in the far south, is about 300,-000 times as bright as the Sun; yet it is so distant that we cannot see it at all without a telescope.

On the other hand, we must not be too humble. If the Sun is not exceptionally bright, neither is it exceptionally faint. Indeed, it is above the average rather than below, even though we class it officially as a dwarf. Some stars are known whose luminosities are only a minute fraction of that of the Sun.

The diameters of the stars are equally diverse. Some, such as the vast red component of the binary system Epsilon Aurigæ, are so large that they cover an area in space much larger than that swept out by the Earth's orbit; others, the so-called "white dwarfs," are planetary in size, a few known being smaller than the Earth. Yet the range in mass is not nearly so great. Large stars are highly rarefied, while the tiny white dwarfs are almost incredibly dense.

It used to be thought that a star began its life as a large, cool "red giant," and contracted to white heat before cooling down once more and ending its active career as a feebly-shining "red dwarf." Nowadays, we know that stellar evolution is not nearly so simple as this; in fact, the Sun is definitely getting hotter as it ages, and instead of being frozen to death our remote descendants (if any survive) are likely to be fried. We have even found out something about the way in which a star shines. In normal stars, such as the Sun, the mechanism involves the changing of the light gas hydrogen into the slightly heavier gas helium, energy being released in the process. Further explanations would be out of place here, and reference should be made to a specialized volume (see Suggestions for Further Reading, Appendix A).

It is often supposed that a powerful telescope should show a star as a measurable disk, rather like that of a planet. Nothing could be farther from the truth. The stars are so inconceivably remote that no telescope yet made will show them as anything but points of light, and if a small instrument shows a star as a distended, shimmering disk, there is something very wrong! In fact, the larger and better the telescope, the smaller the apparent size of the star.

Looking at coloured stars can be a fascinating occupation. For instance, Vega, the brilliant star in the constellation Lyra, is bluish; Capella is yellow; Arcturus, orange; and Betelgeux, Antares, and Aldebaran, orange to orange-red. Intensely blue or yellow stars are not found, while there is no normal star which can really be called "green" (the third-magnitude Beta Libræ comes nearest to it). Red stars, however, are common. Their hue is due simply to the fact that their surfaces are comparatively cool. The reddest star visible to the naked eye is Mu Cephei, not far from Polaris, described by Herschel as "garnet"; optical aid is, however, necessary to show the colour well.

For colour observations, reflectors are naturally better than refractors. Atmospheric conditions must also be taken into account. Even a pure white star, such as Sirius, will show red and green flashes when low down in the sky, simply because it is seen shining through a deep layer of atmosphere.

DOUBLE STARS. The best and most vivid colours, however, are to be found with double stars where the true hues are often accentuated by contrast effects. Perhaps the most beautiful double in the sky is Albireo (Beta Cygni), which lies in the constellation of the Swan, roughly halfway between the two first-magnitude stars Vega and Altair. Here we have a third-magnitude yellow star, accompanied by a blue 5½-magnitude companion at a distance of 34″. This is an easy object in almost any telescope, and never fails to draw a gasp of wonder from the beginner who observes it for the first time. Other beautiful coloured doubles are Eta Persei (magnitudes 4 and 8¾; orange and blue; 28″), Gamma Delphini (4½, 5½; yellow, greenish; 10½″), Gamma Andromedæ (2¼, 5; orange, greenish; 9¾″), and Epsilon Boötis (3, 6¼; yellow, blue; 2¾″). The bright reddish stars Antares and Alpha Herculis have smaller greenish companions.

Double stars, so called, can be divided into two categories: optical doubles, and binaries. The two components of an optical double merely happen to lie in the same line of sight as seen from the Earth, and are not genuinely connected at all, one star being much closer to us than the other. On the other hand, the two (or more) components of a binary system are physically connected, and revolve round their common centre of gravity. Since the stars are not very unequal in mass, it is incorrect to say that the lighter star revolves round the heavier.

The apparent distances of double stars show a wide range. Some, such as Alpha Capricorni (magnitudes 3 and

4; distance 6′ 16″), can be divided with the naked eye. Others, such as the components of Capella, are so close together that they cannot be divided except with the world's largest instruments; and there are many stars which are known to be binary systems, because of spectroscopic effects, but whose components are so close together that no instrument yet made will split them.

The most famous double star in the sky is probably Mizar, the second star in the tail of the Great Bear. Mizar itself is accompanied by a fainter star, Alcor, which is about 11′ distant, and can be seen by anyone with normal eyes; telescopically, Mizar itself proves to be double (magnitudes 2 and 4, distance 14″). A 2-inch telescope will also show several other stars in the field.

Some amateurs make a hobby of measuring the position angles of double stars, using micrometers; but it must be admitted that this work has already been so well covered by the professionals that so far as bright pairs are concerned, at least, little remains to be done. On the other hand, double stars are extremely useful for testing the performance of a telescope. A 2-inch refractor should show the faint companion of Polaris and the two components of Epsilon Boötis; a 4-inch should show the companions of Theta Aurigæ and Delta Cygni; a 10-inch should split Zeta Sagittarii, and so on. A list of convenient "test objects" is given in Appendix C.

Before leaving the subject of double stars, mention should be made of the famous "double-double," Epsilon Lyræ, which lies close to the brilliant Vega. Epsilon Lyræ consists of two small components, Epsilon^1 and Epsilon^2, which can just be distinguished by people with very keen sight. In a small telescope, each component is again divided —Epsilon[1] into two stars of magnitudes 4½ and 6½, 3″ apart; Epsilon[2] into components of magnitudes 5 and 5¼, at a distance of 2¼″. Between the pairs are several other stars, three of which may be seen with moderate apertures.

VARIABLE STARS. Turning now to variable stars, we find that opportunities for doing useful work are much greater. Before describing what observations can be made, however, it will be advisable to give a very rough-and-ready classification of the main types of variable stars:

(1) The Eclipsing Variables. The best example is, of course, Algol (Beta Persei). These stars are not intrinsically variable at all—the diminution in light is caused by the periodical eclipse of the bright star by a dimmer companion —and a better name for them is "eclipsing binaries." All those within range of small telescopes have been closely studied by professional astronomers.

(2) Cepheids. These stars take their name from the best-known member of the class, Delta Cephei (another prominent example is Zeta Geminorum). Cepheids are intrinsically variable, and are very regular in period. A definite law connects the period of a Cepheid with its real luminosity; once the period is known, therefore, the distance of the star can be determined, and the Cepheids are regarded as the astronomer's "standard candles" in space. Since the periods of Cepheids are known to within a second, and the variations can be predicted with complete accuracy, there is little point in the amateur's observing them regularly. This also applies to the sub-class known after the prototype star, RR Lyræ.

(3) Long-Period Variables. With these stars, there is no

law linking period with luminosity, and they have thus been less closely studied at the great observatories. The best-known member of the class is Omicron Ceti (Mira), which varies from magnitude 4 down to 9½ in a period of 333 days. Both magnitude and period are, however, subject to irregularities; the maximum brilliance may sometimes be as great as magnitude 3 or brighter (on one occasion it rose to 1.7). Neither is the period constant. These inconsistencies are common to all the long-period stars, and it is in this field that the amateur can do work of great value. Other bright examples are Chi Cygni and Upsilon Hydræ. It is correct to say that much of our knowledge of the behaviour of these stars is due to amateur observers of such organizations as the Variable Star Section of the British Astronomical Association, and the American Association of Variable Star Observers.

(4) Semi-Regular and Irregular Variables. As their name suggests, these are stars whose fluctuations cannot be predicted with any certainty. Gamma Cassiopeiæ, for instance, seems to be utterly irregular; Moore, who has observed it since 1935, finds that it varies from magnitude 1.6 to 3.3, without any semblance of a period. In the southern hemisphere there is an even more extraordinary star, Eta Argus, which has been known to surpass or at least equal Canopus, but is now totally invisible to the naked eye. On the other hand Betelgeux and Alpha Herculis, both red stars, have very rough periods of about five years. Telescopic semi-regular variables are numerous. The SS Cygni and U Geminorum stars usually remain at their "normal" or minimum brilliance, but have frequent short-lived max-

ima which cannot be predicted accurately. R Coronæ stars may be described as SS Cygni stars in reverse; their normal brilliancy is their maximum, but at irregular intervals they drop sharply in brightness, taking some time to recover. RV Tauri stars have alternate deep and shallow minima; but occasionally the two types of minima are interchanged, for some reason still unknown. Z Camelopardalis sometimes halts its usual fluctuations, and remains at a "standstill" for months on end. Clearly, these semi-regular and irregular stars are of the greatest interest—one never knows just what is going to happen!

(5) Novæ, or New Stars. The name is a misnomer, as a Nova is not a new star at all. What happens is that a very faint and apparently unimportant star suddenly undergoes a tremendous upheaval that increases its brilliancy enormously—perhaps by over ten magnitudes. After a comparatively brief but very violent maximum, the brilliancy falls slowly back almost or quite to its original value. Needless to say, novæ cannot be predicted, and their discovery is largely a matter of luck. For instance J. P. M. Prentice, then Director of the Meteor Section of the British Astronomical Association, was taking a nocturnal stroll on December 13, 1934 (following a period of meteor observing) when he suddenly saw a third-magnitude star shining in Hercules where no star should be. This nova, now known as DQ Herculis, remained visible to the unaided eye for some months. In late 1935 Moore, using a 3-inch refractor, remembers seeing it shining with a lovely green colour, though it had by then dropped below naked-eye visibility. Like most other novæ, it can still be observed, although it is now beyond the reach of small telescopes.

Instruments for measuring star brilliancies, known as photometers, are not easy to make, and the amateur will generally find it much better to keep to estimates, since with practice such estimates can be made accurate enough for almost all purposes. The fundamental method is to compare the variable with other stars of known brilliancy.

Star brilliancies are measured in magnitudes. The scale has a definite mathematical relationship; each star of given magnitude is 2.512 times brighter than a star exactly one magnitude fainter, so that a star of magnitude 1 is 100 times as bright as a star of magnitude 6. (Other types of magnitude—absolute, photographic, bolometric, and the rest—do not concern us here.)

Bright variables, such as Betelgeux, may be followed with the naked eye, and for this purpose it may be useful to give a list of "standard stars" for the various magnitudes:

Magnitude 1: Aldebaran (slightly too faint), Altair (too bright).
Magnitude 2: Alpha Ursæ Majoris, Delta Canis Majoris, Beta Aurigæ.
Magnitude 3: Gamma Boötis, Gamma Ursæ Minoris, Beta Canis Minoris.
Magnitude 4: Theta Boötis, Gamma Canis Majoris, Gamma Aquarii.
Magnitude 5: Upsilon Aurigæ, Epsilon Canis Minoris, Omicron Cephei.

When estimating the brightness of a naked-eyed variable, care must, however, be taken to allow for "atmospheric extinction." The closer a star is to the horizon, the more of its light will be lost. The following table gives the amount of extinction for various altitudes.

Altitude above horizon, Degrees.	*Diminution, in magnitudes.*
1	3
2	2.5
4	2
6	1.5
10	1
11	0.9
13	0.8
15	0.7
17	0.6
19	0.5
21	0.4
26	0.3
32	0.2
43	0.1

Aldebaran is of actual magnitude 1.1. At an altitude of only 1 degree, therefore, it would look theoretically of magnitude 4.1—in actuality less, owing to the almost certain presence of haze. Above an altitude of about 40 degrees, extinction can be neglected. When estimating the brightness of a naked-eye variable, it is obviously advisable to select comparison stars at about the same altitude as the variable itself.

Telescopic variables are in some respects easier, inasmuch as they can be compared with stars only in the same field of view, and the difference in altitude is so small that extinction can be neglected. A 3-inch refractor or a 6-inch reflector is adequate to cover more variables than can be handled by any one observer in the course of a lifetime. As a wide field is desirable, low powers are best—30 or 40 diameters on a 6-inch reflector.

The procedure is as follows. First, obtain a chart of the variable in its star-field (such charts can readily be obtained from appropriate organizations, provided that it is intended to carry out serious regular work). The variable can then be located. Some trouble may be experienced at the very first attempt, particularly if the telescope is altazimuth, but star-fields do not change—and can be recognized without difficulty once they are known. The magnitudes of the comparison stars are known, from the chart. The eye can be trained to estimate differences of magnitude in "steps" of 1/10, 2/10, or 3/10 of a magnitude, and the brilliancy of the variable is deduced. Suppose we are observing a variable of about the eighth magnitude, and have available two comparison stars, one of magnitude 7.5 and the other of 8.2; we are using a "step" of 1/10 mag., and estimate that the variable is 3 steps fainter than the brighter comparison star but 4 steps brighter than the fainter comparison star. The magnitude of the variable is thus 7.8.

Many books have been written about variable stars, and for further information some specialist work must be consulted. It is hoped, however, that we have said enough to make it clear that there are great openings for the amateur in the rich field of variable star astronomy.

Clusters and Nebulæ. Our star system, the Galaxy (often miscalled the Milky Way), includes large numbers of those beautiful objects known as star clusters and galactic nebulæ. Everyone knows the Pleiades, or Seven Sisters, which lie not far from Aldebaran in the constellation of Taurus, the Bull. Needless to say, the stars in the cluster are physically connected, and not merely in a similar line of sight. Six or seven Pleiades can be seen with the unaided eye (Heis, a German astronomer of the 19th century, is said to have seen as many as eighteen), but even a home-made spectacle-lens telescope will reveal dozens more. As a matter of fact, the Pleiades cover too wide an area to be imposing telescopically; it is impossible to get the whole cluster into the field at once. It is thus clear that for observing clusters, the magnification used should be as low as possible.

A finer telescopic sight is the Sword-Handle in Perseus (Herschel VI, 33–34), in which two rich clusters are seen in the same low-power field. Another celebrated loose cluster is Præsepe, in Cancer. Of different type is M.13 * Herculis, a "globular" cluster consisting of a large number of stars apparently closely packed towards the centre. Any small telescope will show it as a blur of light, though an instrument of fair size is needed to resolve it into separate stars.

Galactic or gaseous nebulæ are equally imposing. The finest example is, of course, M.42 Orionis—the Sword-Handle below Orion's belt—which can be seen with the naked eye as a filmy patch, and which contains the famous "Trapezium," the multiple star Theta Orionis. Another gaseous nebula is M.27 Vulpeculæ, not far from Altair, which is known as the Dumb-Bell Nebula for reasons which will be obvious to anyone who has seen it. Some so-called galactic nebulæ, however, are not worthy of the name. The famous "Ring Nebula" near Vega, between the stars Beta and Gamma Lyræ, can be seen faintly in a 2½-inch telescope; larger instruments show it looking like a smoke

* The designation "M.13" indicates that the object was No. 13 in Jean Messier's famous catalogue of star clusters and nebulæ.

ring, and it is in fact what is known as a planetary nebula, a star surrounded by an extensive gaseous shell. On the other hand, the Crab Nebula, M.1 Tauri, is merely the gaseous wreck of a supernova (a nova of exceptional violence) which was observed by the Chinese as long ago as the year 1054.

Our own stellar system, the Galaxy, is by no means unique. It is our own galaxy among untold millions, and far away in space we can see other galaxies which must be fully the equal of our own. Many of these external systems are spiral in shape, looking in large telescopes like gigantic celestial Catherine wheels. They are immensely distant; the nearest of the really large ones, M.31 Andromedæ, is almost 2 million light-years away. M.31 is the only external galaxy visible with the unaided eye. Telescopically, it is rather a disappointment. It is placed at an angle to us, so that the spiral effect is largely lost, and small telescopes will show it only as an ill-defined blur of light. Perhaps the most imposing of the face-on spirals is M.51 Canum Venaticorum, not far from Alkaid (the end star in the tail of the Great Bear), but even this will not reveal its true form except in a powerful instrument.

This book is concerned with practical work open to the amateur with a moderate telescope, and it would thus be beyond our scope to enter more fully into a discussion of the clusters, the galactic nebulæ and the external galaxies; but even if little useful work can be done except at the great observatories, there is always immense satisfaction to be found from looking at these vast systems as they glow dimly across the void of space. The starry heavens are fascinating indeed; we have learned much, but there is so much that we do not yet understand.

X

SPECIAL EQUIPMENT FOR OBSERVING THE SUN

THE Sun is a dangerous object for the amateur observer, as the incautious use of even the smallest telescope can result in partial or total blindness. Precautions have to be taken to safeguard the eyesight, while special equipment is required for what may be called the analysis of this stupendous globe.

To protect the eye against the excessive light and heat, the ordinary dark glass can be used with apertures up to 2 inches, but anything larger will result in the glass cracking if the observation is prolonged. With reflecting telescopes, unsilvered mirrors prove effective, but the flat should not have parallel faces, as otherwise a double reflection will result. A polarizing eyepiece can be used, but its cost makes it a luxury beyond the reach of most amateurs; and all things considered, the solar diagonal is the best solution.

With either a diagonal or a projection device, the details of sunspots and faculæ can be studied, but this is as far as sheer telescopic observation will take us. The early morning hours are generally the best for solar observation, as the air has not heated up, and consequently definition is at its best.

But many amateurs would like to be able to observe the prominences, those towering pillars of glowing gas (chiefly hydrogen) which spring from the layers of similar gas surrounding the bright surface or "photosphere." Opticians ask a high price for the necessary apparatus, and such observations are usually regarded as being beyond the amateur's means. In actual fact, however, any amateur can make the apparatus for himself at a small cost.

The Sun is made up of various elements at a high temperature and in a gaseous state. Each element emits rays of characteristic wave-lengths, that is, characteristic colours, and the cumulative effect is "white" sunlight. That ordinary sunlight really consists of rays of all colours is shown by passing it through some transparent substance, such as glass, shaped so as to have sides inclined to each other—in other words, a prism. If this is done, the "white" ray which enters at one face emerges from the other as a coloured streak known as a "spectrum." Different transparent substances vary in their degree of effectiveness in this respect. Dense flint glass will give a much longer spectrum than a similar prism made of ordinary or crown glass, while a solution of carbon disulphide contained in a hollow prism gives a spectrum longer even than that produced by flint glass. Being a liquid, it has however the disadvantage that heat sets up currents which destroy the purity of the spectrum, so that in practice prisms of dense flint glass are usually employed.

The prominences emit rays in the red, blue, and violet parts of the spectrum. The reason they cannot be seen with a telescope is because their feeble light is completely drowned in the general glare. If we can manage to tone down the general light while at the same time maintaining the prominence light at full intensity, it should be possible to see the prominences by their light alone; and this is precisely what a spectroscope does. The simple but effective instrument described below will afford excellent views of the strange, fascinating prominences if used in conjunction with a small telescope (refractors of 3 inches upwards or reflectors of 6 inches).

The essential part of the equipment consists of four dense flint glass prisms, of 60° angles, having two of the three faces polished. We also want two safety-razor blades, an ordinary single convex lens of about 4 inches focus and an inch or so in diameter, and some form of viewing telescope. The latter may consist of a similar lens mounted in a tube with an eyepiece at the other end.

Obtain a piece of brass tubing of diameter sufficient to hold the lens, and fix the lens in position by rings, as described in Chapter II. The two safety-razor blades should be mounted in a little frame, allowing for one of them to be moved so that the distance between the two can be varied from actual contact to perhaps ⅛ of an inch apart. This frame must now be fastened at the other end of the tube, at a distance from the lens such that when we look through the lens the blades seem sharply defined. This combination of blades and lens is known as the "slit and collimator."

Now obtain a brass sheet or a nicely planed board, and fasten the tube to it by means of little brackets. We also need some means of securing the plate (or board) to the telescope; we therefore fix a short piece of tubing, of such diameter as to fit the eyepiece tube of the telescope, in front of the slit and in line with the tube.

Now place the first prism base inwards, edge outwards, and with face inclined to the lens tube. The exact inclination must be found by trial, and will vary according to the part of the spectrum under observation. The prism can be secured by making a little wire frame, with triangular top and bottom, and securing it by a screw. Do the same with the remaining three prisms; look through the last prism, direct the slit to some bright light, and adjust the prisms until the red and yellow portions of the spectrum are best placed. If the blades almost touch, a number of dark lines will be seen when sunlight is examined; these lines run vertically across the spectrum band, and are caused by the various elements in the Sun. Hydrogen, for instance, gives a line in the red part of the spectrum, while sodium gives two lines close together in the yellow.

Now make up the viewing telescope (a toy telescope will do quite well, if to hand), and, using a movable bracket, fix it to the base so that it points towards the last prism. Adjust and focus until the lines in the spectrum are sharply defined. The lines will appear narrow when the blades almost touch, but with wider separation of the blades the lines become "bands" of greater breadth.

On a bright sunlit day, fix up the apparatus and direct the telescope to the Sun. No eyepiece must be used. Adjust the apparatus until the image of the Sun is sharply focused on the slit. On looking through the viewing telescope, the solar spectrum will be seen. If the Sun's image falls on only part of the slit, we will see a brilliant spectrum at one part and a faint one above, due to the illuminated atmosphere. Now bring the line due to hydrogen, in the red part of the spectrum, central in the viewing telescope. It may be that when the Sun's image falls only partly on the slit, the hydrogen line in the faint spectrum above it will suddenly light up like a red-hot wire. This means that there is a prominence at this part of the Sun's limb.

To see the prominences in their true guise, we must adjust the apparatus so that the image of the Sun is almost touching the blades—that is to say, wholly on one blade, and just touching the other. If there happens to be a prominence at that point, it will glow; and if the slit is opened, the prominence will be seen as a whole. Should the actual edge of the Sun intrude, the ordinary solar spectrum will fill the field. The secret of successful prominence observation consists of bringing the Sun's edge to touch but not overlap the slit, subsequently sweeping around the image so as to examine every portion of the limb in turn.

So far we have been concerned with the prismatic spectroscope, but an alternative form may be used, replacing the prism by a diffraction grating. This grating is a metal or glass plate ruled with a large number of lines very close together—in some cases, many thousands to the inch. Whereas a prismatic instrument produces one spectrum only, a grating produces several spectra of different lengths, none of which is as bright as that produced by a prism. The grating has, however, the advantage of forming a spectrum dispersed truly according to the wavelengths, whereas with prisms the red end is unduly compressed and the short-wave or violet end unduly extended.

A more elaborate instrument is the spectrohelioscope, by means of which a very considerable arc of the Sun's limb can be scanned at any one time. Essentially, this instrument consists of a train of prisms (or a grating) and two slits. The first slit is placed so as to receive the focused image of the Sun; the rays then pass on to a mirror, which is slightly inclined so as to reflect on to the prisms (or grating) where the spectrum is formed. The spectrum is then reflected from another mirror on to the second slit, which can be adjusted to allow light of only one particular wavelength to pass. In this way we can isolate the line due to (say) hydrogen or calcium, and examine the Sun in the light of that element only. Since the result would be a thin line, the two slits are either given a rapid movement from side to side, or else prisms in front of the slits are rapidly rotated so that, owing to persistence of vision, the lines are converted into broad bands covering a considerable portion of the Sun.

Another instrument was devised by the late Dr. Bernard Lyot, the brilliant French astronomer. This is known as the monochromator. It is a filter, and consists of a series of quartz plates, each double the thickness of the preceding one; by polarization, it is able to isolate the particular band in the spectrum due to any desired element. With this instrument, it is possible to see prominences not only around the limb, but on the disk as well. It is too difficult for amateur construction, as is also the case with the spectrohelioscope; and the majority of amateurs content themselves with the ordinary spectroscope.

Although the coronagraph (also invented by Dr. Lyot) enables us to study the inner corona without a total eclipse, it, too, is beyond the capability of any amateur. Even if made, it still could not be used except on top of some lofty mountain, above the dust-laden lower atmosphere.

With the aid of the apparatus described here, however, the amateur will be well equipped to observe both spots and prominences, thus ensuring many hours of interesting research. It is fitting to conclude with a final warning as to the dangers of looking directly at the Sun through any telescope, even when fitted with a dark "sun-cap." The authors know of at least two men who have permanently impaired their eyesight in this way.

XI

PHOTOGRAPHS THROUGH THE TELESCOPE

ALTHOUGH careful and accurate drawing is still the best way in which an observer can record what he sees, it is not the only method; photography can be employed. Of course, the amateur equipped with a small instrument cannot hope to secure pictures which will rival the magnificent photographs secured by the use of the giant telescopes of to-day, but he can obtain records which are not only interesting but which possess definite scientific value. While his pictures of starfields must fall far short of professional efforts, those of eclipses or comets may be the equal of any. It is possible that he might be the only observer favoured with a clear sky, in which case the value of his photographs will be obvious.

In effect, celestial photography merely means the substitution of a photographic plate or film for the eye; but there are some differences between it and ordinary photography. To begin with, the objects we want to photograph are in motion, and it is impossible to make them stand still. This means that with a fixed telescope, short exposures are essential, so that only bright objects can be photographed. During an eclipse of the Moon, successful photographs can be taken merely by the use of the simple spectacle-lens telescope described in Chapter II, a cut film or plate in a suitable holder being attached to the eye end. The exposure is made by a cap over the object-glass being whisked off for a fraction of a second. A rapid panchromatic film or plate will give the best results.

For better telescopes, we can construct a simple camera, which is merely a metal box with grooves to take a plate-holder, or dark slide, at one end, and a piece of tubing to fit the eyepiece tube of the telescope at the other. In the apparatus used by Wilkins, this piece of tubing itself carries another grooved plate so that the plate-holder can be inserted in this if photographs at the focus, without an eyepiece, are desired. If we want an enlarged picture, the plate-holder is placed at the other end of the box, and an eyepiece is used in the ordinary way. The grooved plate then carries a strip of metal with a slot, which acts as a shutter by being slid through the groove.

By varying the focus of the eyepiece, different degrees of enlargement can be obtained; but the greater the enlargement, the longer must be the exposure. Hence we are limited to photography of the Sun and Moon. If the final image is not more than 1½ or 2 inches across, an exposure of ¼ second will give good results, provided that rapid plates and fine-grain developer are used. If the instrument is a refractor, pre-focusing on a ground glass screen will not be reliable, owing to the difference between the visual and photographic foci; hence a yellow filter should be used.

If our telescope is driven in any way, longer exposures can be given, and we can photograph planets, comets, and star-fields. The exposures may be anything from a minute to several hours, depending upon the subject. With an exposure of half an hour, a great number of star images will be recorded, and the excellence of the drive will be proved if the images appear as dots! It is perfectly easy, of course, to photograph stars with a fixed camera. If pointed towards the celestial pole and left for an hour, the plate when developed will show a large number of short curved trails, arcs of circles with the pole as the centre; there may be a straight trail cutting the curves, in which case we will unwittingly have secured a photograph of a meteor.

With a fixed 6-inch reflector with a focal ratio of *f*/8 or less, it is easy to photograph the Moon. A plate-holder at the focus, without an eyepiece, using a fine-grained film, should be used; an exposure of $1/10$ of a second will give a sharp picture capable of some enlargement. We cannot enlarge it much, however, or the grain will intrude; it is thus better to use an enlarged image upon the film. With a reflector, there is no chromatic aberration, and hence the image at the focus can be focused visually on a ground-glass screen. If we want an enlarged image, we must employ some kind of eyepiece, and the introduction of this lens may introduce aberration, as well as requiring a longer exposure. We may use a Barlow achromatic negative lens placed within the focus to enlarge the primary image; alternatively, we can employ a positive eyepiece. An orthoscopic eyepiece magnifying the primary image 6 or 8 times will be satisfactory, the exposure being $1/5$ second on a film such as Super XX. If the instrument is driven, we can use slow and finer-grained emulsions, and expose for 1 to 2 seconds. Control during developing is essential, the aim being to record detail all over the image and not merely along the terminator.

To photograph the Sun, very short exposures and slow films or plates are essential. The telescope may be stopped down; exposures from 1/100 to 1/25 of a second on even lantern plates will record the sunspots in detail. Experience can only be gained by actual trial.

In all cases, the best focus can be found by trial exposures, when with any given arrangement of eyepiece and plate-holder the precise position from some fixed part of the telescope can be prominently marked. Needless to say, everything must be rigid, and not subject to the slightest warping or displacement.

To photograph a comet, we must guide the telescope to follow the slowly moving comet; the stars will thus come out as short trails. We want a good finder fitted with cross-wires, and we must have an equatorial mounting. Exposures range from 1/2 to 2 hours, during which time the comet must be kept accurately behind the cross-wires. It will soon be found that it is distinctly tedious to keep one's eye glued to the eyepiece for an hour or more at a time, especially during the winter months; but it is the only way to obtain a satisfactory result.

To photograph a whole constellation, we can use an ordinary camera, provided it has a fairly long focus, strapped to an equatorial mounted telescope. A star is brought to the centre of the field of view, and the camera focused for infinity. Exposures of half an hour will record a large number of star images.

The earthlit crescent Moon, perhaps with a bright planet

such as Jupiter or Venus near it, makes an attractive picture, and can be photographed with a lens of from 10 to 20 inches focus mounted at one end of a home-made camera attached to a telescope for guiding purposes. The camera is merely a cardboard box, with the lens at one end and a film holder at the other, the focus being found by trial. The difficulty is to avoid excessive over-exposure of the bright crescent; the most satisfactory exposure length must again be found by trial. Slow developing and thorough fixing are needed, and it is hardly necessary to add that with panchromatic emulsions developing should be done in total darkness.

The amateur's apparatus may be made up from cardboard, wood or metal, and such lenses as may be available. Second-hand service lenses can often be obtained, and mounted in suitable light-proof boxes or tubes fitted with a simple device to hold the plate or film. A 35-mm. film is favoured by some people. Such plates as Ilford HP/3 are suitable for celestial photography, and may be developed in Kodak D.76a or similar solutions. The grain will allow considerable enlargement before becoming troublesome.

Every amateur celestial photographer should be prepared to do his own developing. Every care should be taken to avoid dust settling on the emulsion. The camera device should be clean, the film only exposed to the air during the actual exposure, and developing should be done in an atmosphere as dust-free as possible. The plate should be rocked during developing and fixing. Drying should be done in similar clean conditions, for every speck on the negative will show up, especially in enlargements.

If a satisfactory negative is obtained, it may be enlarged

in the usual manner; also, lantern slides may be made by direct contact in the printing frame. If a dark-room is not available, developing, enlarging and loading can be done at night.

Generally speaking, observers in the country have conditions far better than those of the town dweller. In a city, prolonged exposures usually reveal a certain amount of fogging of the plate, whereas in the country the absence of artificial lighting enables much fainter objects to be recorded and longer exposures to be given. Whether in town or country, the greatest care must be taken to avoid any shaking of the apparatus; hence hurry and distractions should be avoided. Better wait an extra half-hour for the desired cup of tea than spoil an otherwise promising photograph!

To sum up: celestial photography is within the reach of everyone. Much of the apparatus can be made at home; visits to junk shops are often valuable for suitable lenses, and parts of old cameras can often be picked up cheaply. Whether films or plates are favoured, they should be kept as dust-free as possible. Make everything too sturdy and rigid rather than the opposite, so as to eliminate vibration. Finally, the operator must possess plenty of patience, and must be ready to balance his successes against his failures.

XII

OBSERVATORIES

To THE ordinary person, the very word "observatory" conjures up a picture of a great domed structure standing by itself on the top of a lonely mountain, entirely isolated, and used only by men who spend night after night peering through the main eyepiece and making careful, complex drawings of the Moon, planets and stars. Yet this picture is wrong in several respects. To begin with, most of the world's largest telescopes, such as the Palomar 200-inch and the Mount Wilson 100-inch, are very seldom used visually at all, but are employed as giant cameras; the astronomer's work consists of fixing and adjusting the photographic plates, and then watching through the finder to make sure that the object under study is kept firmly in position while the exposure is being made. Lunar and planetary drawings made with great apertures are few and far between; systematic visual work is not attempted, as all the available time is needed for photographic studies of stellar spectra and extragalactic nebulæ.*

The picture is untrue in another way. An observatory

* This is not true of one or two special observatories, such as the Pic du Midi, where Dr. Dollfus and his colleagues make their magnificent planetary observations, and the Lowell Observatory in Arizona; but it is the general rule. The Moon has been particularly neglected. So far as we know, the series of observations made with the Meudon 33-inch by the authors in 1952 and 1953 was the first time that a large instrument had been used for such a purpose for over forty years.

consists not of a single dome containing one great instrument, but of a multitude of domes and buildings, containing different types of telescopes and cameras, dark-rooms, laboratories, optical workshops, living quarters and the like. In fact, an observatory is almost a city in itself. Nor is it correct to say that all are lofty and isolated; Meudon, with its powerful 33-inch refractor, lies within a few kilometres of Paris and from the outer park the lights of the Eiffel Tower can be seen winking in the distance.

Yet the great establishments, from Palomar downwards, are of only indirect interest to the amateur, who will probably never be able to visit them. The true meaning of the word is far wider. The first observatories were indeed set up long before the invention of the telescope, and were equipped with positional measuring instruments with which star catalogues were made. The Arabian caliph Al-Mamun built an observatory at Baghdad in the ninth century and another was constructed in the fifteenth century by the ill-fated Ulug Beg at his capital city, Samarkand. The first European observatory was built at Nuremberg in 1472 by Bernhard Walther. The most famous of all pre-telescopic observatories, however, were those of Uraniborg and Stjarneborg, erected by Tycho Brahe on the Danish island of Hven. Uraniborg was completed in 1576, and contained much equipment, as well as various refinements not to be found at Palomar or Mount Wilson (such as a gaol; Tycho was also virtual ruler of the island, and to say that he was hated by the people of Hven would be to put it mildly). Uraniborg was abandoned in 1597, when Tycho left his native country for good, and to-day nothing remains of the original structure.

Naturally enough, the true story of the observatory properly so called begins with the invention of the telescope. During the 17th century, many were set up in Europe. The universities of Copenhagen and Leyden took the lead; the French national observatory at Paris was completed in 1671, and that at Greenwich four years later. The story of the founding of Greenwich is in fact curious, as has been outlined elsewhere by one of the authors;* Flamsteed, the first Astronomer Royal, was provided with a building, but had to provide the instruments himself—with the result that his widow removed them after his death, leaving his successor, Edmond Halley, to begin again. As time went by, instruments were improved. Equatorial mounts were developed by Römer in 1690; clock drives followed a century later, and the early primitive observatories grew into the great organizations that they are today.

Yet as well as national and university observatories, there were—and are—many observatories built and used by private individuals. In fact, anyone with patience and a certain manual skill can construct an observatory if he so wishes. To give a detailed account of how to do it would be beyond the scope of the present work, as it belongs more properly to a builder's manual, but a few general hints can be given.

If the observatory is to be a proper affair with a revolving dome, it should have a solidly constructed base, preferably of brick, while the upper part and the dome itself can be far less substantial. The dome should be capable of easy movement; nothing is more irritating than a contrivance which

* Patrick Moore, *The Story of Man and the Stars,* Norton, New York, 1955.

persistently sticks and requires a great deal of brute force to haul it around. If rails are used, they should be kept well greased. The swinging can be done by hand—automatic driving is certainly not necessary—and the section of the dome which is to be capable of removal may either be swung back on hinges, or (under certain circumstances) taken out altogether. The inside of the observatory should on no account be heated, as the hot air will rise and swirl out through the opened slit, causing a stellar or planetary image to look as though describing a wild waltz in the heavens.

Now and then, of course, unusual observatories are found. One, used by Moore between 1946 and 1949, stood on the exact crest of a hillock, so that to one side the roof was level with the ground, while to the other there was a steep incline equipped with slippery steps. The method of opening the dome was to swing it round until the removable slit was level with the hilltop, when the entire slit could be lifted away from outside. (It was also possible to fall through the dome in the process, as was ascertained—inadvertently—by practical experience.)

However, a revolving dome is far from a necessity, and considerations of space will generally rule it out. Much simpler buildings can be devised. As has been pointed out in Chapter III, it is not essential to have an observatory at all, even with a fair-sized instrument; Wilkins' 15¼-inch reflector has stood in the open for years without coming to any harm. On the other hand, it is in some ways a good idea to give the telescope some protection against the weather. One excellent service is the run-off shed.

Refractors are more cumbersome than reflectors, principally because they are longer and heavier, and it is probably true to say that a 4-inch is the largest size that can be considered even remotely portable. With a 5- or 6-inch, some sort of observatory or covering is needed. Reflectors are shorter and less solid, so that they are easier to handle; the upper limit for a portable instrument is about 8 to 9 inches.

The usual trouble encountered when an observatory is to be built is that there are few places with a horizon that is clear all the way down. Trees, houses and other obstructions always appear in the most inconvenient spots. The selection of a site must therefore depend upon the nature of the work to be undertaken. Planetary and lunar observers—such as the authors—are interested mainly in the ecliptic, so that a situation with a clear southern horizon should be sought; variable-star observers, on the other hand, require the north as well, and have to compromise. Once a large, heavy telescope is set up it is not easy to shift, particularly if an observatory of any kind is involved, so that considerable initial thought should be given to the problem.

In general, however, the run-off shed is to be recommended as an excellent observatory, while if even this cannot be managed, and it is considered desirable to cover the telescope, a waterproof tarpaulin will serve. Ingenious persons may, of course, have their own ideas upon the subject. One 10-inch reflector known to the authors is actually mounted upon a wheelbarrow!

In the United States some observers have mounted their telescopes on top of automobiles.

XIII

USING LARGE TELESCOPES

EVERYONE who is interested in astronomy must have wished, at some time or other, to look through a really great instrument. Amateurs are familiar with the appearance of the Moon as seen through a 6- or 8-inch reflector, but they wonder what it must be like through one of the world's largest telescopes; they draw Mars, but would be glad to have the opportunity for a few minutes' observation with, say, the 40-inch refractor at Yerkes or the 33-inch at Meudon. Few amateurs do have such opportunities. The great telescopes are used by the professional workers, and are committed to specialized investigations for months in advance. If amateurs were allowed the use of these valuable instruments, it would mean not only the attendance of a member of the observatory staff but also serious dislocation of the observing programme. Some institutions, such as the Lick Observatory in California, do devote a few hours per week for amateurs to view some object through the great telescope, but this means taking one's place in the queue and hastily squinting at whatever object the attendant has picked. This is often some double star or star-cluster, while the object that interests our amateur far more may be in another part of the sky, shining down with tantalizing brilliance. Such peeps, however gratifying, are of no real use, and neither is a daylight tour of such an observatory any substitute for the amateur's desire. It must also be remembered that most of the people who attend "public nights" are mere sightseers, without any genuine interest in astronomy.

It would, of course, be possible to equip an observatory with a smaller but still considerable instrument, and use it for the benefit of amateurs. Many people might thus be attracted towards the study of the heavens.

On the other hand, there are certain amateurs who are invited to use great instruments, on the understanding that this is for the express purpose of clearing up disputed points and filling up gaps in their records. Among the amateurs so privileged have been the authors of this book, both of whom have made extensive lunar and planetary observations with the Meudon 33-inch and some also with the two large instruments at Cambridge University. During a tour of America in 1954, Wilkins also observed with the Mount Wilson 60-inch, the Yerkes 40-inch refractor, the Washington 26-inch refractor and other instruments of large aperture.

What is the advantage of large instruments, and in what ways do they exhibit their superiority over the small or medium-sized telescopes in the possession of most amateurs?

Large telescopes have a tremendous power for gathering light. They can thus reveal faint objects which cannot be seen at all in lesser instruments, and can show the shapes and forms of objects which look no more than spots in small telescopes. If we want to see the satellites of Mars, for instance, it is no use looking for them with a 6-inch reflector, even when the Red Planet is at its nearest. (Deimos, the smaller of the two moonlets, is particularly elusive; observing under fairly good conditions in 1952 with Wilkins' 15¼-inch reflector, the authors succeeded in glimpsing it,

Fig. 24. Observing Mars with the 60-inch reflector at Mt. Wilson Observatory, Cal., U.S.A., June, 1954

but not easily.) Minute lunar details also required large apertures, as do the surface features of the satellites of other planets.

The great 33-inch refracting telescope of the Meudon Observatory, near Paris, is the third largest of its kind in the world (the largest in Europe), and is a supreme example of the optician's art. The objective was made by the Brothers Henry, and has a focal length of about 52 feet. All these giant instruments are very heavy, and it takes time to adjust them; the mounting of the Meudon telescope weighs over 20 tons, and a mass like that cannot be lightly swung over one's head! But once directed, with the driving mechanism in operation, the views of celestial objects are superb indeed. In April, 1952, the authors, accompanied by Madame Hermann and Dr. Bertaud of the Observatory, turned the telescope to the Moon. The first glance showed the well-known crater of Plato, looking so large and so clear that it wanted but little stretch of the imagination to believe that we were looking at it from a helicopter hovering at a great height. The tumbled masses forming the encircling mountain ring, their harsh and black shadows and the little crater-cones sprinkled over the nearly level floor or interior, each with its tiny spot of shadow, were crystal clear. The finder attached to the great telescope is a 5-inch refractor, and looking through it all that could be seen within Plato were one or two tiny dots whose nature it was impossible to determine. Yet a 5-inch refractor is a telescope of considerable power, with which much useful work may be done.

With the 5-inch finder, the bright rings of Saturn could be seen, and also indications of the dusky or Crêpe Ring. The satellites were also visible, shining like stars. In the great telescope the Crêpe Ring was a conspicuous object, while the satellite Titan, in particular, showed an obvious yellowish disk. Upon this disk, Wilkins recorded two dusky spots, which were however invisible to Moore *—sufficient testimony to the difficulty of the observation, even with the 33-inch.

With the Meudon telescope, many of the lunar regions popularly believed to be smooth and undisturbed were seen to be in reality rough and uneven, sprinkled over with little pits and rent by narrow chasms or clefts. So great was the amount of detail that both of us worked as hard as possible drawing various objects during the ten clear nights during which we used the telescope in 1952 and 1953, yet could cover much less than 1/500 of the entire surface of our satellite. Many of the details appearing on our sketches had never been recorded before, simply because nobody had looked for them with a large telescope; but this need not discourage the amateur with a 6-inch, for his instrument, too, is capable of showing many objects in various regions not yet appearing on the lunar maps.

During a lecture tour in the United States in 1954, Wilkins was able to go further, and observe the Moon with the 60-inch reflector at Mount Wilson. With this great aperture, features which showed no detail from Meudon were resolved in exactly the same manner as the Meudon instrument surpassed those of smaller size. With the Yerkes 40-inch refractor, wonderful views were obtained of Mars; the canals were revealed streaking the disk, a great cloud hung over the limb, and the little moon Deimos could be seen shining close to the planet's face. Saturn, too, was

* My eyesight is appreciably less keen than that of Dr. Wilkins, and any slight differences in visual acuity are evident when the observations concerned are of great delicacy.—P. M.

magnificent. The disk was richly detailed, with numerous belts, dark spots, and wisps or threads in the equatorial zone. The rings were displayed with a clarity never seen before. In addition to the major division (Cassini's), the much more delicate division of Encke and a still finer in Ring B were visible, as well as a distinct break between Ring B and the inner or Crêpe Ring, which appeared brownish. Again, detail was seen on Titan. Perhaps this wealth of detail was to be expected, since the Yerkes refractor is the largest in the world.

Large instruments can only reveal their superiority under good conditions; if the seeing is not first-class, large refractors perform better than reflectors, because there is far less disturbance inside the tube. At the same time, it must not be imagined that under even indifferent conditions everyone will see the same. Skilled observers always see more than casual viewers, whatever the instrument. Trained observers who were with Wilkins when using the Yerkes refractor agreed entirely with his drawings, but others also present could not see so much. For example, the skilled observer T. Cave saw Deimos clearly, but casual viewers could not. It is a matter of practice and training of the eye. With the 60-inch reflector at Mount Wilson there was a good deal of what astronomers call "boiling" when Wilkins was observing—a general confusion of detail, as though everything were in rapid motion, though periodically this would subside, leaving the outlines crystal clear for a short time. Here again only the trained observers could see what Wilkins showed in his sketches, and doubtless a person with a more acute eye would have found details overlooked by him.

Fig. 25. Observing the planets with the Yerkes 40-inch telescope, the largest refractor in the world, in July, 1954

When it is a matter of detecting difficult details, such as minute spots and strokes on a small disk, the ability to do so varies widely between observers. Details of this sort are the delicate markings on the moons of Saturn and Jupiter and on the disks of the far-away planets Uranus and Neptune. Large telescopes are essential for this work, and we can discount the often very remarkable features seen on the four great satellites of Jupiter with small instruments such as 6-inch reflectors. No one will doubt the honesty of an observer who covers Ganymede or Callisto with spots and dots as observed with such a telescope, but it is very easy to "see" what one half expects to see, and the temptation to record detail which is no more than suspected should always be resisted. This is particularly so in the cases of Venus and Mars. The streaky, spokelike markings of Venus found on many drawings made with telescopes of less than 10 inches aperture simply do not exist—they are optical effects; and the drawings of Mars made with similar apertures which show canals in profusion are entirely worthless.

A great deal of nonsense has been written and spoken about large instruments. For example, it has been stated that under all save the best atmospheric conditions, definition is poor and the resolution lost, so that only low magnifying powers can be used, and in place of the sharp outlines given by small telescopes all that can be seen are flowing light spots. The facts are that even under mediocre conditions, large instruments (particularly refractors) often perform excellently, and more can be seen with comparatively low powers than with high powers on smaller telescopes. The same applies to large reflectors, even though under mediocre conditions there is indeed a good deal of flowing of the image; now and then the definition settles down and becomes critically sharp for a few moments, so that even on a poor night more can be seen with a large reflector than with a small one. These remarks are based upon personal observations made by the authors, and not upon mere hearsay.

It has even been maintained that a large telescope will never show as much lunar or planetary detail as a smaller one, owing to the greater disturbance of the image by atmospheric tremors! This somewhat unintelligent suggestion hardly merits further discussion. Nor is it generally necessary to "stop down" a large aperture; the only effect is to reduce the light-gathering power of the instrument, and there is no real advantage. It is significant that Lowell, at Flagstaff, habitually stopped down his 24-inch refractor to only 18 inches—and his drawings have been called into question; for example, he covered Venus and the Jovian moons with linear streaks that are definitely nonexistent. The authors, observing from Meudon with a larger refractor under conditions that were sometimes far inferior, had not the slightest inclination to stop down the aperture of the 33-inch.

Large instruments, whether reflectors or refractors, do not require great magnification to resolve fine details. We never used more than 540 to 600 on the Meudon refractor, and did a great deal of our work with a power of 320. On the 60-inch reflector at Mount Wilson Wilkins employed a power of 500, which is only a little over 8 per inch of aperture, yet was sufficient to show details quite beyond the reach of smaller telescopes armed with powers similar to or even higher than that used on the large telescope. We could see far more with a power of 320 on the 33-inch than with a power of 600 on Wilkins' 15¼-inch reflector or 400 on Moore's 12½-inch, simply because the superior light-gathering capacity and resolving capability of the great instrument produced details in the image which were lacking in the images formed by smaller lenses or mirrors. No sensible person would dream of using higher powers than are necessary to reveal the details sought for; the lower the power used, the steadier the image, and the easier the observation. Since large apertures will show objects clearly defined under lower powers than with small telescopes under similar magnification, and it will in addition show details beyond the range of smaller instruments, there is no need to push the magnification upwards to a point where the image becomes blurred and diffuse. Were this not the case, there would be no advantage in using a large telescope; indeed if we follow the argument to its logical conclusion, there would be no benefit in using a telescope at all—we might as well use the naked eye! The objective or mirror of a telescope is a sort of artificial eye, which is superior in light-gathering power to the human eye because it is so much larger. It thus gathers more light, and its focal length is much longer than that of the eye, so that it gives a picture on a larger scale.

It thus follows that every telescope has a certain limit of performance, depending upon its aperture; and although details recorded up to this limit are trustworthy, all other details seen beyond the limits of the resolving power of the instrument must be illusory. We see now why the Martian and satellite observations so often produced with tiny telescopes of aperture 6 inches or less must be discounted if they show fine details such as canals.

Yet there is abundant work for the small telescope to do; the heavens are always changing, there is always something new to see, and a vast amount of work remains to be done, much of it within the range of our amateur equipped with a 6-inch reflector. Naturally, scope is widened by increased aperture, and to all amateurs we say: Make or get as large a telescope as you possibly can, and make the most of any opportunities to observe with still larger instruments. By so doing, your interest in the subject will be greatly stimulated, and your personal knowledge will be enhanced.

APPENDIX A

SUGGESTIONS FOR FURTHER READING

IT IS naturally impossible to give an exhaustive list of all astronomical works which will be found useful; to do so would require many books the size of the present one! The following suggestions may, however, prove helpful. Books marked * are out of print, but may be obtained from many public libraries as well as the libraries of astronomical societies.

(1) *General Astronomy*

BUDELER, W. *To Other Worlds.* (Burke, 1954; translation by A. L. Helm.) An excellent general survey of modern astronomical problems, with a description of the 200-inch telescope at Palomar. There is a section devoted to problems of space-flight.

DAVIDSON, M. (Editor). *Astronomy for Everyman.* (Dutton, 1952.) A concise general astronomy written for the popular reader. Contributors include directors of observational sections of the British Astronomical Association.

PAYNE-GAPOSCHKIN, C. *Introduction to Astronomy.* (Prentice-Hall, 1954.) A book by the Phillips Astronomer at Harvard University. It is detailed, and perhaps the best general astronomical work that has yet appeared.

JONES, SIR HAROLD S. *General Astronomy.* (St. Martins, 1951.) A comprehensive general astronomy. A book by the Astronomer Royal must surely need no extra recommendation.

WILKINS, H. P. *Mysteries of Space and Time.* (Muller, 1955.) A general review of some of the outstanding problems of modern astronomy, with the results of work carried out by the author and others using very large telescopes.

(2) *Planetary Astronomy*

VAUCOULEURS, G. DE. *The Planet Mars.* (Macmillan, 1950; translation by Patrick Moore.) An excellent semi-popular account of Mars.

VAUCOULEURS, G. DE. *Physics of the Planet Mars.* (Macmillan, 1954.) A technical study for the advanced reader. This is undoubtedly the most important work yet published on the subject of Mars.

MOORE, PATRICK. *Guide to the Planets.* (Norton, 1954.) A detailed account of the planets, written for the general reader who wishes to make actual observations with a small or moderate-sized telescope.

MOORE, PATRICK. *Guide to Mars.* (Muller, 1955; in press.) A popular summary of what is now known about Mars, with a map of the surface features.

RICHARDSON, R. S. *Man and the Planets.* (Muller, 1954.) An excellent general account of the planets and problems of getting to them in the future.

SPENCER JONES, SIR H. *Life on Other Worlds.* (English Universities Press, 1952. New American Library, paperbound.) An account of the possibilities of life elsewhere in the universe.

STRUGHOLD, H. *The Green and Red Planet.* (University of New Mexico, 1954.) A study of the possibilities of life on Mars, written by a distinguished biologist who is also an astronomer.

(3) *Lunar Astronomy*

ELGER, T. G. *Map of the Moon.* (Philip and Son, 1955.) The book to illustrate this map is long since out of print, but the map, revised by Wilkins, is readily obtainable. It is a most useful outline chart of the surface features, and all amateur observers will find it of great value.

*GOODACRE, W. *The Moon.* (Privately published at Bournemouth, 1930.) A description of the lunar surface, accompanied by Goodacre's famous map.

MOORE, PATRICK. *Guide to the Moon.* (Norton, 1953.) A popular account of the Moon intended for the observational amateur as well as for the general reader; there is a small-scale map of the surface features.

*NEISON, E. *The Moon.* (Longmans, Green and Co., 1876.) The first classical work in English, and still of great value. There is a detailed description of the surface, and a comprehensive map based upon Mädler's.

*PICKERING, W. H. *Photographic Atlas of the Moon.* (Annals of Harvard College Observatory, 1903.) A series of photographs showing each part of the Moon under five different conditions of lighting.

WILKINS, H. P. *Our Moon.* (Muller, 1954.) A popular account of the Moon intended both for the general reader and for the observational amateur. It contains a small-scale map, and the results of the author's work with very large telescopes.

WILKINS, H. P., and MOORE, PATRICK. *The Moon.* (Macmillan, 1955.) An exhaustive description of the lunar surface, illustrated with the Wilkins' 300-inch map on a reduced scale and with many drawings and photographs by all eminent observers of the present day.

(4) *Stellar Astronomy*

DOIG, PETER. *Stellar Astronomy.* (Hutchinson, 1947.) An excellent introduction to astronomy, written for the reader with knowledge slightly more than that of the beginner.

PAYNE-GAPOSCHKIN, C. *Stars in the Making.* (Harvard, 1952.) An account of modern problems of stellar astronomy and cosmology.

SMART, W. M. *Some Famous Stars.* (Longmans, Green and Co., 1950.) A survey of modern stellar problems, written for the general reader.

(5) *Historical Astronomy*

DOIG, PETER. *History of Astronomy.* (Hutchinson, 1951.) A concise general history of astronomy.

ABETTI, G. *History of Astronomy.* Sidgwick, translator. (Macmillan, London, in press.) A comprehensive history of astronomy, written by a distinguished Italian astronomer.

MOORE, PATRICK. *The Story of Man and the Stars.* (Norton, 1955.) A survey of the past, present and future problems, written for the general reader.

(6) *Star Atlas*

NORTON'S STAR ATLAS. (Gall and Inglis.) By far the best star atlas for the amateur. It has run to many editions, and is almost a necessity both for the beginner and for the serious observer.

(7) *Instruments*

Much information can be derived from *The English Mechanic,* which can be consulted at most large public libraries. Wassell, a pioneer in mirror making, wrote between 1881 and 1883, and other authorities between 1890 and 1907.

The first adequate work was *The Amateur's Telescope,* by Ellison, published by Carswell and Son in 1920. This was afterwards extended and improved by the magazine *Scientific American* with the title *Amateur Telescope Making—Advanced.* The most recent edition, edited by A. G. Ingalls, appeared in 1954.

A little book, *Preparation of Mirrors for Astronomical Telescopes,* by McHardie (Blackie and Son, 1937), will be found useful.

APPENDIX B

USEFUL INFORMATION

The Dialyte Telescope

In an attempt to avoid the expense of an achromatic objective, which in large sizes is very considerable, the Dialyte form of instrument was invented.

This consists of a single, non-achromatic, plate-glass convex lens, either plano-convex or double-convex, which by itself would form an image suffering from both spherical and chromatic aberration. Between the lens and the focus is placed a small achromatic lens, composed of a convex of crown glass and a concave of flint glass, and known as the corrector, because it corrects the errors of the large single objective. The cost of the corrector is much less than that of an achromatic combination of aperture equal to that of the large objective.

For anyone who wishes to experiment, the following formulæ will be found useful. The Dialyte was once popular in Germany.

If δ = ratio of the crown and flint dispersive powers of the correctors,

F = focus of the large single objective,

f = focus of either of the lenses of the corrector,

a = distance between the objective and the corrector,
A = radius of the single objective,
C = radius of the corrector lenses,

$$(1)\qquad \delta = \frac{f(F-a)^2}{Ff-(F-a)^2},$$

$$(2)\qquad F = \left[\frac{A^2}{C^2}\left(\frac{1-\delta}{F\delta}\right)\right].$$

The Fullan Test for Optical Surfaces

This differs from the Foucault Test in the illuminated pinhole being placed at the focus instead of at the radius of curvature. The concave surface of the mirror returns a parallel beam which is intercepted by a plane mirror, from which it is returned to the mirror. Being a parallel beam, it resembles the light received from a celestial body, and the concave mirror returns it to the focus. Hence the knife-edge will show the surface darkening evenly all over, if the figure is parabolic.

Some Useful Formulæ

(*a*) Proportion of dextrose and silver nitrate solution for silvering—10 drms. 10% dext. to 5 oz. silver nitrate, or 1 gram solid dextrose to 2½ grs. solid silver nitrate.

(*b*) Size of Solar (or Lunar) image in inches, when the focal length (L) of the telescope is known.

Diameter of image (inches) = (tan. Sun's diameter in minutes of arc) × L.

(*c*) Size of Flat—Major Axis = 1.414 × Minor Axis.
A = aperture of parabolic mirror,

F = focal length,
a = aperture of field lens of eyepiece of lowest power,
D = distance of flat from focal point,
X = minor axis of flat.

$$X = \frac{D(A - a)}{F} + a$$

Working Large Mirrors

If a mirror disk is available but not another disk to act as a tool, one can be made up of concrete to the desired size. Cover with pitch, and stick on glass squares, ⅛ inch apart. After grinding, cover with pitch in the usual manner.

APPENDIX C

LIMITING MAGNITUDES AND TEST OBJECTS

IT IS naturally difficult to give a definite limiting magnitude for any aperture, since much depends upon the keenness of the eye. A good observer will see more than an indifferent one under the same conditions. The following list may, however, be found helpful. "Aperture" refers to the object-glass of a refractor.

Aperture in Inches	*Limiting Magnitude*	*"Test" Double Stars*
1.5	9.0	Beta Orionis (Rigel). Magnitudes 0, 8. Separation 9″.1.
2	9.7	Gamma Leonis. Magnitudes 2½, 2¾. Separation 3″.7. Alpha Piscium. Magnitudes 3, 4. Separation 3″. Delta Cassiopeiæ. Magnitudes 3, 7½. Separation 9″.5. Alpha Ursæ Minoris (Polaris). Magnitudes 2, 9½. Separation 18″.6.
2.5	10.2	Alpha Serpentis. Magnitudes 3, 10. Separation 58″. Epsilon Boötis. Magnitudes 3, 6½. Separation 3″.
3	10.6	Alpha Tauri (Aldebaran). Magnitudes 1, 10½. Separation 109″.

Aperture in Inches	*Limiting Magnitude*	*"Test" Double Stars*
		Eta Pegasi. Magnitudes 3, 10. Separation 90″.
		Theta Virginis. Magnitudes 3, 9. Separation 7″.
3.5	10.9	Alpha Lyræ (Vega). Magnitudes 0, 10½. Separation 52″.
4	11.3	Iota Ursæ Majoris. Magnitudes 3, 10. Separation 10″.8.
		Gamma Ceti. Magnitudes 3, 7. Separation 2″.6.
		Delta Geminorum. Magnitudes 4, 9. Separation 7″.
		Sigma Cassiopeiæ. Magnitudes 6, 8. Separation 3″.1.
4.5	11.5	Mu Andromedæ. Magnitudes 4, 11. Separation 37″.
		Tau Boötis. Magnitudes 4¾, 11½. Separation 10″.3.
5	11.8	Epsilon Persei. Magnitudes 3, 8¼. Separation 8″.8.

Further limiting magnitudes are as follows: 6 in., 12.2; 7 in., 12.6; 8 in., 12.9; 9 in., 13.2; 10 in., 13.4; 11 in., 13.6; 12 in., 13.8; 13 in., 14.0; 14 in., 14.2; 15 in., 14.4.

APPENDIX D

MAKING A SIMPLE PLANETARIUM

IN CERTAIN countries, many cities have a Planetarium, which is a device by means of which a representation of the heavens is presented to an audience. The stars and planets are represented by light spots projected on the interior of a hemispherical dome, while the Sun is represented by a larger and brighter spot. The projectors can be set in motion so that the stars appear to revolve around the pole, and the impression is a realistic representation of the actual sky.

While a full-sized and complete projector is an expensive and complicated apparatus, it is not difficult to construct a simple home-made planetarium for use in an ordinary room. The lights are extinguished; at the touch of a switch, the ceiling and upper walls suddenly become the night sky with the Big Dipper, Orion, and other constellations clearly depicted and in slow rotation, some rising above the eastern horizon and others setting in the west, while the star-groups around the pole circle round and round without reaching the horizon, just as the real circumpolar stars do. There is some distortion, owing to the ceiling and walls not forming part of a dome, but this defect is unavoidable; and our home-made instrument will prove an unfailing source of enjoyment to family and friends.

Despite the surprising results, the instrument is very easy to make; it requires no special tools, and can be constructed on the kitchen table in a few hours. Neither is there any danger in operation, the apparatus being run from a flashlight battery.

The actual projector is merely a tin of about 6 inches diameter, pierced by a number of small holes and with a flashlight bulb inside. When it is lit, light streams out of the holes, and spots appear on the ceiling and walls. The holes are spaced to correspond to the real constellations, the brighter stars having larger holes than the fainter ones. The faintest stars require holes made by a needle point, while the brightest stars may be projected by holes of about ⅙ inch diameter made with the point of a compass or scriber. To set out the holes in their correct relative positions, the centre of the top of the tin is taken as the pole, and the Pole Star represented by a rather small hole close to it. The centre of the side of the tin will be the equator, and the tin should be first marked with a pencil to indicate the meridians of right ascension and the parallels of declination. The positions of the stars are then marked on the tin in their correct places as given by a star map, only they must be reversed from left to right. For example, the Big Dipper, which on the map appears thus . · · . : will be marked on the tin : . · · · and will then be projected in the correct way.

About two or three hundred holes will be sufficient, although we can put in more if we have enough patience to do so. The lid is then put on the tin, a hole being made in its centre to take the shaft or axis by means of which the instrument can be rotated. In Wilkins' instrument, this axis was an ordinary flashlight, the cover and reflector being removed so that the bulb was exposed and also placed well above the end of the flashlight, which fitted tightly into the hole in the lid of the tin. The bulb should be in the equatorial plane.

A simple wooden or metal stand, with one face inclined at an angle equal to the latitude of the place of observation, is now made, and the flashlight turns in brackets of some sort fastened to this face. The brackets may be made from strips of metal or leather straps, and the torch can rest on V-blocks secured to the stand. This will enable the torch, and with it the tin, to be rotated.

On pressing the switch, the stars appear in a most realistic manner, because the bulb is almost a point of light. If we attempted to run the device off the mains with an ordinary lamp, it would be found that the holes would act as pin-hole cameras, and the comparatively long filaments would be projected on to the ceiling instead of spots. The actual filament or source of light should be as small as possible.

If we want to insert the Sun, Moon or planets, a number of similar but of course much smaller projectors must be made, one for each object, and pierced with holes of appropriate size. For the Moon, the hole may be in the form of a crescent; alternatively we could have a larger hole and a plate pierced with holes in the shape of the crescent, half-moon and so on, arranged to rotate in front of the fixed hole. We can also fit a lens in front of the plate to ensure that a sharp image is projected.

These special projectors can be secured by brackets to another shaft inclined to that of the star-sphere, at the proper angle of 23½ degrees, in order that the motions of the Sun, Moon, and planets may be confined to the Zodiacal constellations. Each projector must have its own bulb, con-

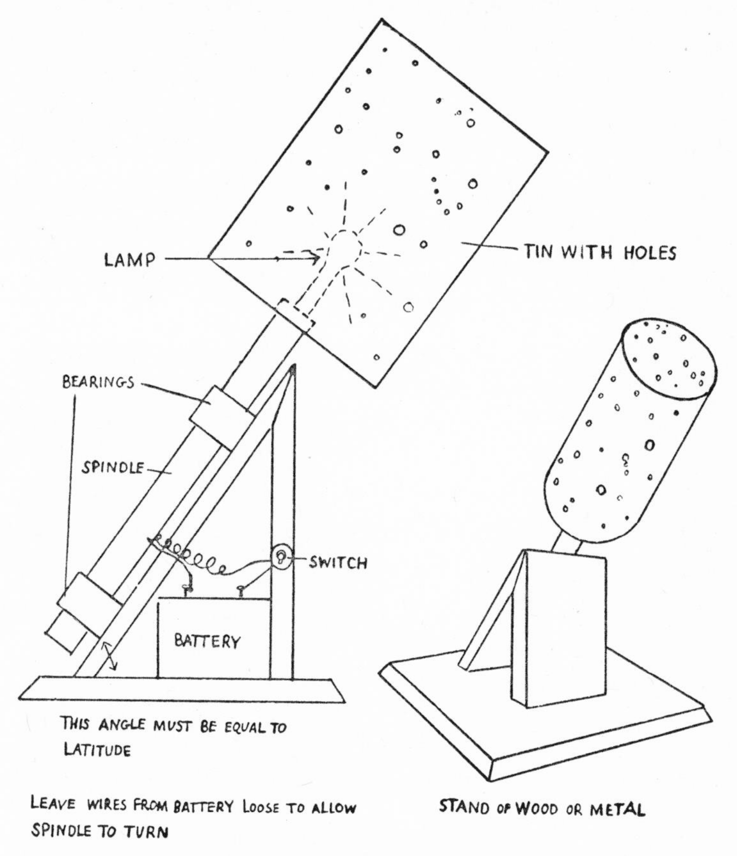

Fig. 26. Planetarium

trolled by a switch so that it may be brought into operation when desired.

A better projector will result if instead of a tin we use

a hollow sphere, such as a cistern ball of suitable diameter. The most simple but also the most expensive way would be to obtain a celestial globe, and pierce the star-dots already on its surface. Fixed to an axis and with a lamp inside, our projector would be ready for action.

When made, the planetarium will give best results in a small room, for the greater the distance of the ceiling and walls the larger and fainter will be the light spots. The ideal distance is about 6 feet from the source, whether this be ceiling or wall; but even in an ordinary room the results will be spectacular, and will fully justify the slight amount of time and labour involved.

APPENDIX E

ASTRONOMICAL SOCIETIES

IT IS advisable for our interested amateur to join an astronomical society. The advantages gained are manifold. He will not only receive the latest information and be put in touch with other observers, but also he will receive help and advice if he wants it.

The leading amateur society in England is the British Astronomical Association (B.A.A.), founded in 1890 and now comprising over 2000 members spread throughout the world. In addition to the amateurs, it includes a great number of professionals (the Astronomer Royal is a Past President). Observational sections are guided by experienced directors, and at the moment the directors of the planetary sections are: Mercury and Venus, P. Moore; Mars, E. H. Collinson; Jupiter, Dr. A. F. O'D. Alexander (assisted by W. E. Fox); Saturn, M. B. B. Heath; the Moon, Dr. H. P. Wilkins (assisted by Moore as Secretary and F. H. Thornton as editor of the Lunar Section periodical). These Sections issue memoirs from time to time, and also publish their results in the Association's monthly Journal; the Lunar Section also issues its own periodical. The B.A.A. also includes an Instruments and Observing Methods Section, directed by Dr. W. H. Steavenson, which deals with matters such as telescope construction and mounting.

The nearest American equivalent of the B.A.A. is the Association of Lunar and Planetary Observers (A.L.P.O.), directed by Professor W. H. Haas, with its headquarters at Las Cruces, New Mexico. Its periodical, the *Strolling Astronomer,* is a mine of information, and here again there are specific Sections directed by experienced recorders: Mercury, J. T. Carle; Venus, Dr. J. C. Bartlett; Jupiter, C. Brooks; Saturn, T. L. Cragg; Mars and the Moon, Professor W. H. Haas.

The Astronomical Society of the Pacific, with its headquarters in San Francisco, is an eminent association including some of America's foremost astronomers. Its bimonthly *Publications* contain information of extreme value upon all branches of astronomy, while the mainly non-technical monthly Leaflets will be of particular interest to the amateur.

In the United States, where there are some 100,000 amateur astronomers, there are astronomical societies in more than 100 cities. Most of them are affiliated into a federation under the name of the Astronomical League, which has its headquarters in Silver Spring, Maryland. Another notable organization is the Amateur Astronomers' Association, with its offices at the Hayden Planetarium in New York City.

No specific technical qualifications are needed for membership in these societies; the main requirements are enthusiasm and patience.